GREAT BARRIER ISLAND

GREAT BARRIER ISLAND

EDITOR
DON ARMITAGE

CANTERBURY UNIVERSITY PRESS

First published in 2001 by
CANTERBURY UNIVERSITY PRESS
University of Canterbury
Private Bag 4800
Christchurch
NEW ZEALAND

mail@cup.canterbury.ac.nz
www.cup.canterbury.ac.nz

ISBN 1-877257-03-6

Cover photographs: North Island kaka, green gecko (Len Doel);
kokako (Murray Douglas);
aerial view of east coast (Brent Baker)
Halftitle page: view of Great Barrier from Rakitu (George Medland)
Title page: Sunset, Tryphena (Fullers)
Contents page: photo by Tony Bouzaid

Designed and typeset by Mark Winstanley/Go Ahead Graphics
Printed in New Zealand by Rainbow Print, Christchurch

Publication of this book has been supported by a grant from the
Lotteries Heritage and Environment fund

CONTENTS

EDITOR'S ACKNOWLEDGEMENTS

This book would not have been possible without the co-operation of many individuals, organisations and companies, both on and off Great Barrier Island. Firstly the authors, whose knowledge and dedication you will appreciate as you read on; the Great Barrier Island Community Board and especially Tony Bouzaid for his unfailing support. I also acknowledge the assistance and advice of Great Barrier residents Jacqui Ackland, Brent Baker, Dave Barker, Alan and Grace Benson, Beverly Blackwell, Charlie Blackwell, Keith Briars, Kevin and Gwen Burke, Garth and Pat Cooper, Mike Gardiner, Ngaire Gibbs, Judy Gilbert, Martin Gillard, Alan and Sue Gray, the late Bob Harrison, Adrienne Johnson, Bert Jordan, Greg Laird, Whetu McGregor, Scott MacIndoe, Bruce MacNee, Teresa Manion-Wood and Dennis Mendoza, George Mason, George, David and Dean Medland, Marty Mitchener, Michael and Helen O'Shea, John Powell, Shannon Robertson, Johnny Scott, Peter and Helga Speck, David Speir, Sven Stellin, Chris and Sue Thompson, Mary Walshaw, Pauli Whaanga, Bob Whitmore, Chrissie Young. Also Bill Ballantine, Len Doel, Gordon Ell, David Hill, Tania Mace, Sarah Macready, Alicia Major, Graham Murdoch, Keri Neilson and Adele Smaill; David Towns, Tony Whitaker, the Great Barrier Island DOC staff, especially Don Woodcock, and Auckland DOC staff members, especially Marie Alpe, Chris Green and Bec Stanley; ARC staff members Karen Baverstock, Mike Lee and Ngaire Sullivan; the Great Barrier Service Centre staff of Auckland City; John Early and Stephen Thorpe of the Auckland Institute and Museum and Grant Pearce of the Forest Research Institute.

The assistance of the ferry company Gulf Trans and airline companies Great Barrier Airlines and Mountain Air in getting authors, photographers and researchers to and from the island is gratefully acknowledged, as is the financial assistance by way of a grant from the Lotteries Heritage and Environment fund to the Hauraki Gulf Charitable Trust (special thanks to Anna Cassels-Brown), and Millennium funding from Auckland City. Last but not least I would like to thank the staff and associates of Canterbury University Press, especially Mike Bradstock, Richard King, Paula Wagemaker and Mark Winstanley.

Great Barrier is probably my favourite island in the whole world. Not just because it helps make the Hauraki Gulf such a wonderful marine playground by sheltering it from the ocean swell, but also because of the many special places there.

From the wonderful views and the unique bush at the top of Mt Hobson, to the kauri dams, the bush streams, the wetlands and the hot springs, there are many good tracks where you can experience the New Zealand wilderness the way it should be experienced — on foot.

Great Barrier is easy to reach by air or water, and is a place where you really feel alive. The wildlife is very special too, with kaka, rails, brown teal, lizards and native frogs to name just a few.

Thinking has certainly changed since the days of the axe, the match and the miner's pick. The bush is regenerating and a good start has been made to getting pests such as goats under control. Fortunately some of the worst pests like weasels, stoats, Norway rats and possums have never become established on Great Barrier. We must do everything possible to keep the island free of these destructive animals. We also need to eliminate pests like wild cats, kiore and ship rats that are still there.

Then, as long as we can prevent fires and control our pet dogs and cats responsibly, nature will just about take care of the rest all by itself.

While we enjoy Great Barrier, let's not forget to look after it for future generations.

Peter Blake

The bush is silent now. Gone are the sounds of axe and saw, the pounding of the stamping battery and the whistle of the logging trains. Gone also is the birdsong that echoed throughout this island before the habitat of native species was destroyed.

While the native bush is regenerating, some predators have come to complete the work of man and ensure extermination of the surviving endangered species. The rat and cat, goats, pigs and dogs are still decimating our remaining wildlife.

As custodians of the largest offshore island of New Zealand it behoves us all to follow the example set by a few pathfinders to help turn the tide on the reducing numbers of our native wildlife. The state of the environment at the turn of the millennium records that Great Barrier Island is still free of the imported predators, possum, stoat, ferret, weasel, deer, Norway rat and hedgehog, that have devastated mainland native wildlife. While legislation has been enacted to protect this status it is hoped that further efforts will

Offshore islands along the western coast of Great Barrier. Coromandel Peninsula in the background.

Brent Baker

be made by the Territorial Local Authorities and the Department of Conservation to eradicate or at least control the remaining predators.

The Great Barrier Community Board is sponsoring this book to celebrate the turn of the millennium and to provide the public with a better understanding of Great Barrier Island as a unique and special place in the heritage and natural history of New Zealand. We recognize that this island has a history of exploitation of natural resources but fortunately we are still not too late to accept the challenge of restoration that must take place during the 21st century. Great Barrier Island is the last populated bastion where many of our endangered species can co-exist with us, New Zealand's Noah's Ark.

When will we learn to take responsibility for the carnage? When will we learn to neuter and control our pets? When will we learn that it is up to us to eliminate the pests and provide a small space of New Zealand where our native species can live with us and survive?

CHAPTER ONE

GREAT BARRIER ISLAND

Great Barrier Island, the largest island off the coast of the North Island, was named by Captain James Cook for the barrier it forms between the Hauraki Gulf and the open sea. The island is located at the tip of the Coromandel Peninsula in the sea known traditionally as Te Moana nui o Toi, the great sea of Toi. Originally part of the Coromandel Ranges, the island has a mountainous spine. Its highest peak, Hirakimata (Mt Hobson), at 621 metres, dominates the rugged forest-covered terrain. Great Barrier is about 40 kilometres long, about 15 kilometres in maximum width, and measures about 285 km^2.

Great Barrier includes 23 islands and numerous islets and rocks. The main island is named Aotea, which means 'white cloud' but is associated in local tradition with the *Aotea* canoe, which visited the island in the thirteenth century. The relative isolation and ruggedness of Great Barrier Island have kept it largely undeveloped and free from many of the animal pests that have taken their toll elsewhere in New Zealand. As a result there is a superb natural landscape, a high number of rare native plants and animals and numerous well-preserved historic sites.

In local tradition, Aotea was first occupied by the Tutumaiao, Maewao or Turehu people, who doubtless were attracted by the island's mild climate and abundant food resources. Aotea's equitable climate was well suited to growing crops such as kumara and taro. Although the interior of the island was mountainous and covered with dense bush, areas of relatively flat land suitable for cultivation were to be found around the coast, and the Coromandel and east coasts of Auckland and Northland could be reached easily by canoe.

From the thirteenth century, Aotea was settled by people of Tainui and Arawa descent. Known as Ngati Tai and Ngati Te Wharau, they occupied the island in relative peace for over three centuries. During the late seventeenth century they came into increasing contact with the powerful Ngati Manaia (Ngati Wai) tribe from lower Northland and also with the Marutuahu tribes who were progressively taking control of the Hauraki district.

The death of a Ngati Manaia woman on Aotea in the late 1700s led to a war party of her people attacking Aotea. This group was led by Rehua, the eponymous ancestor of Ngati Rehua, and his son, Te Rangituangahuru. A series of battles followed, culminating in Rehua's people taking possession of the northern half of the island. The peoples of the island eventually intermarried, but the political stability of these links was broken when Te Mata of Ngati Tai murdered Rehua. A large group of Rehua's Ngati Wai and Kawerau relatives avenged his death in a series of battles, which resulted in Ngati Tai and Ngati Te Wharau being forced from the island.

This 1844 painting by George Angas depicts Nga Toenga, daughter of the Ngati Maru chief Waraurangi, from Great Barrier Island. She is wearing clematis flowers on her straw hat.

The descendants of Rehua stayed on Aotea and became known as Ngati Rehua, the tribe that still occupies Aotea today. Four generations after the death of Rehua, Ranginui of Ngati Wai travelled from his mainland home to Aotea to visit his relatives. He was given land, and some of his people settled the island, further cementing familial links. In time, Ngati Rehua became part of Ngati Wai, the present-day tangata whenua of Aotea and the lower Northland coastline and offshore islands. Through intermarriage, Ngati Rehua are also descendants of the older occupants of Aotea, and linked in the same way to the Marutuahu people of Moehau (Coromandel).

During the 1820s and 1830s the Nga Puhi tribe of Northland, newly armed with muskets, travelled south on a campaign of terror, which resulted in the devastation of many North Island tribes. Ngati Rehua were unmolested because of their ancestral relationship with Nga Puhi, and even took place in some of their raids. In 1838 a Ngati Kahungunu war party from Hawke's Bay arrived on Aotea accompanied by a small number of Nga Puhi. They were returning from a 'peace-making' visit to the Bay of Islands, during which they had secured many muskets. At the time most of Ngati Rehua were mutton-birding on the islands to the north. Ngati Kahungunu interfered with the local food stores and humiliated several high-born women, one of whom was from Hauraki. She sent word to her Marutuahu relatives, who joined with Ngati Rehua on their return home. A major battle was then fought at Whangapoua. Losses were heavy on both sides, but Ngati Kahungunu were repelled. After the battle, Ngati Wai feared an attack from Nga Puhi, who had recently hosted Ngati Kahungunu and lost men in the fighting. They consequently left Aotea and took refuge with their Marutuahu relatives at Te Kapanga (Coromandel) and Tangiaro (Port Charles).

The Marutuahu tribes were aggrieved at the heavy losses they had suffered in aiding Ngati Rehua. In compensation the leading Marutuahu chief, Te Horeta Te Taniwha, arranged for the sale of Aotea to his son-in-law William Webster, an American timber trader, and his partners William Abercrombie and Jeremiah Nagle. The actual amount sold is still disputed, but the transaction led to Ngati Wai losing all of their land on the island.

When Ngati Rehua returned to Aotea in 1838, they ignored the sale of all or part of their ancestral home to William Webster and resettled the whole island. The Crown awarded Webster only 4,000 hectares of his 'purchase'. Other Europeans immediately bought much of central Aotea from tribes resident in Coromandel, while the Crown bought the rest of the island, again from Coromandel tribes, in 1854 and 1856. Ngati Wai neither participated in nor recognised any of these transactions, and were left landless. They petitioned the Crown for a reserve on which to live, and in the late 1850s were given a 2,400-hectare part of the Great Barrier Mining Company land at Motairehe (Katherine Bay). This has remained their home ever since, although Ngati Rehua still regard themselves as tangata whenua of all Aotea.

Contact between Ngati Wai and Europeans began in the eighteenth century when whaling ships visited Aotea. Friendly relations were established between sailors and Ngati Wai, with whom they traded for supplies. Reports from ships visiting in the late 1820s described the island as lacking human habitation. It is likely that European diseases brought by the sailors had greatly diminished the island's population.

The nineteenth century brought an influx of European settlers to the colony of New Zealand, searching for natural resources that could be exported to Britain and elsewhere. The alienation of land from Ngati Wai opened the door for more extensive exploitation of Great Barrier Island.

Copper was discovered at Miners Head in 1841, and the first mining operation in New Zealand was established there the following year (see p.28). The mine closed in 1867, but some of the mining families stayed on as farmers. In 1892 silver and gold were discovered in the Okupu/ Whangaparapara area, and the settlement of Oreville at one time consisted of 400 inhabitants. But by 1920 the mines lay abandoned.

Walkway at Windy Canyon on the way to Mount Hobson, a popular spot offering spectacular views.

Tony Bouzaid

The rugged mountainous interior held impressive stands of kauri, which had first been exploited in 1794 when two shiploads of kauri spars were taken for the British navy. Many ships were built on the island from local timber in the following years. Kauri was harvested for export from 1840, and the timber industry lasted a century. The mill opened in 1909 at Whangaparapara Harbour was reputedly the largest in the southern hemisphere. Kauri gum was also dug during the late nineteenth and early twentieth centuries.

Farming (see next pages) also contributed significantly to the island's economy, initially on a subsistence basis as poor communications with the mainland meant that the settlers had to live off the land. Manuka was also cut and sent to the mainland for firewood, to earn cash. Once the land was broken in, the settlers took up dairy, cattle, sheep, poultry farming and bee-keeping. Between the wars, dairy farming was the main industry, but isolation was a problem.

FARMING ON GREAT BARRIER

The regenerating manuka and kanuka scrub that sprawls over half of Great Barrier today was once pasture. The early would-be farmers broke in the land with axe and match. To build their fences they cut puriri into posts and made battens from taraire and rewarewa. Selling firewood to Auckland, transported on motorised sailing scows such as the *Rahiri* and *Jane Gifford*, sustained them until they were able to procure stock. Later these vessels carried mainly cattle, sheep and pigs, the occasional horse and general cargo.

The soil was deficient in essential elements such as molybdenum, cobalt and selenium. It was therefore unable to grow ryegrass or clover, yet supported *Danthonia* grass, which grows well in the summer but has low nutritive value. Stock often suffered from 'grass staggers', a symptom of poor nutrition. Each summer or autumn the farmers burnt the grass, after which the surviving roots would produce a flush of new growth. To sustain soil fertility they also applied basic slag, a mineral-rich by-product from steel-making, and later on, superphosphate.

Pastureland reached its greatest extent in the early 1900s when there were more than 20,000 sheep. Cattle predominated on the flat drained wetlands, while sheep

Operating directly from Ardmore aerodrome, a James Aviation DC3 drops superphosphate over the Medland farm in 1974. In earlier times Tiger Moths topdressed off the Claris airfield.

George Medland

grazed the hills. Goats also were released to crop grass around cliff edges where sheep might otherwise be attracted. The first sheep flocks were mainly Romney, but Romney/Cheviot crosses, farmed for both wool and meat, became popular after the Second World War. Cattle included the docile Shorthorn, as well as Herefords and Black Polls. Hundreds of bales of wool, along with live sheep and cattle, were sea-freighted to the mainland annually. Timber-felling required bullocks, which were turned out to pasture wearing cow-bells. Dairy herds, including Ayrshires, Dairy Shorthorns, Jerseys and Friesians, produced milk from which cream was separated on the island and shipped weekly to Auckland.

Diversification reduced the risk of failure, and many innovative ventures were tried. The Blackwells, near Tryphena, grew their own wheat to make flour for their bakery. Fallen trees hosted large quantities of Jew's ear fungus, which was dried and sold by the sackful to Chinese buyers. Between the wars, some goats were reared for fibre, and later the Crawford family ran fallow deer on Kaikoura Island. Some ventures exchanged one kind of risk for another; for instance, a large moonshine still operated 'somewhere in the north'.

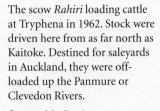

The scow *Rahiri* loading cattle at Tryphena in 1962. Stock were driven here from as far north as Kaitoke. Destined for saleyards in Auckland, they were off-loaded up the Panmure or Clevedon Rivers.

George Medland

Boat-building used large numbers of pohutukawa 'knees' (tough, durable, naturally curved branches which could be trimmed to make ribs), which were plentiful. Many farmers kept hives, and each year up to 10 tonnes of honey went off the island, mostly in 18-litre tins. Half as much again may have been used domestically, often to replace sugar. For a brief period during the early 1980s there was high demand for kashgora fibre from the progeny of feral and angora goats. Many feral goats were captured, usually by helicopter. Some were sent to Arid and Kaikoura Islands, but attempts at farming them there were short-lived as the kashgora market had already passed its peak. Along the way, goats, 'Captain Cooker' pigs and rabbits, along with fish, paua and other seafoods, have supplemented the food stocks of families living on Great Barrier.

After the Second World War, dairy farming became more lucrative, and surplus skim milk was used to fatten pigs for bacon or for sale as porkers on the hoof. The descendants of those pigs, a cross between the Tamworth and Berkshire breeds, are often seen in the bush today. So, too, are the 'Captain Cookers', whose ancestors probably came in 1773 on Captain James Cook's *Resolution* to, it is thought, the Coromandel, and thence to Great Barrier by trade or gift between Maori.

Farming declined in the late 1960s with the demise of the cream industry and increasing problems with frequency of shipping, high freight costs, wrangles between farming families over the location of wharves, and young people looking further afield. Furthermore, the land had become exhausted, a situation that not even aerial topdressing could arrest. Poor soil meant poor lambing rates and difficulties sustaining ewe numbers. As farming became more difficult, the land area in pasture diminished and the regeneration of manuka and kanuka accelerated. Today, the options for farming are severe adaptation or extinction.

There was a short-lived resurgence of whaling, based at Whangaparapara, during the 1950s (see p.26).

The islanders have always had to be self-sufficient for many things other New Zealanders take for granted. They draw their water from streams and storage tanks, use generators, windmills or solar panels for their electricity supply, and many refrigerators are gas-powered. For many years, communications with the mainland depended on boat mail, involving considerable delays in bad weather conditions. The sinking of the SS *Wairarapa* in 1894, with heavy loss of life, led to the introduction of the world's first airmail postal service — by homing pigeons, the sinking having brought home to islanders the need to communicate quickly with the mainland in event of emergency. In 1908 this was supplanted by a telegraph service to the mainland.

The island has had primary schools since 1879, but there is still no local high school. The older children either do correspondence or attend mainland boarding schools. Fast ferries and more frequent flights have brought the island in closer contact with the mainland over recent years, replacing slower sea vessels and the amphibian airline service. The island is still largely dependent on the mainland for its everyday needs.

Movement about the island was particularly difficult before the Second World War, with trips from the main settlements of Port Fitzroy to Tryphena more easily accomplished by catching the ship, which would arrive at Fitzroy and then Tryphena one week, reversing its schedule the next. Until the early 1930s, when relief workers cut a road from Claris to Okupu, the only roads were from Fitzroy to Okiwi and Medlands to Tryphena. During the Second World War the airfield at Claris was built, and the roads were extended from there to Medlands, and from Harataonga to Okiwi. Roads into Katherine Bay and Orama were made after the war. Today, the island's 120 kilometres of road are being progressively sealed, but boats continue to be an important means of transport.

During the last three decades the economy and the social structure of the island have seen considerable change.

In the 1970s several farms were subdivided and there was an influx of people seeking 'alternative' lifestyles. The resident population of Great Barrier today numbers around 1,100. Local families have hosted holidaymakers in their homes since the 1920s, but recently tourism has become more important. Many commercial longline and crayfishermen changed to operating fishing tours, having sold or leased their fish quotas when the quota system came in in the 1980s. Mussel farming thrives with nine farms in Fitzroy harbour and Katherine Bay producing 1500 tonnes annually. Allied to the industry, the 'Great Fitzroy Musselfest' has become a huge annual summer event.

Administratively, Great Barrier is part of Auckland City, which means that the island is run essentially as a suburb of Auckland. Island residents pay rates to the city's council and are represented by a Hauraki Gulf councillor who also sits on the island's community board. About two-thirds of Great Barrier's land falls under the jurisdiction of the Department of Conservation, which is responsible for conserving the natural and cultural heritage of these areas. Until 1942, the Forest Service managed this land, but since that time much of it has been allowed to revert to native bush.

The expanse of sea between island and mainland has helped to minimise development and other pressures on Great Barrier, enabling life on the island to maintain its unique quality. Today, visitors go to the island for the same reasons that people have always lived there — to experience its natural beauty, a sense of times past and a slower pace of life.

Grumman Widgeon aeroplanes by the Oruawharo Stream at Medlands Beach in 1962. These amphibious aircraft provided a vital island link for many years, operated by various companies including Tourist Air Travel, Seabee Air and Mt.Cook Airlines. A larger version was the Grumman Goose.

George Medland

RADIO HAURAKI — NEW ZEALAND'S ORIGINAL ROCK STATION

One of the more unusual but better-known enterprises closely associated with Great Barrier Island is the 'pirate' radio station, Radio Hauraki. It all began in 1965 when Wellington journalist David Gapes sought to establish a private radio station in an effort to break the government's monopoly on commercial broadcasting.

Gapes decided his only option was to operate from a location outside government jurisdiction. That meant transmitting from a ship outside the New Zealand territorial sea, which then extended five miles offshore. He and his team obtained the old scow *Tiri,* and announced their intention to transmit from the Colville Channel, between Great Barrier Island and the Coromandel Peninsula. The government tried every possible bureaucratic tactic to prevent the ship sailing, but in November 1966 *Tiri* finally went on the air. By this time, Gapes' struggle to get the enterprise underway had strong public support nationwide, especially from younger people.

Operating in the frequently rough international waters of the Hauraki Gulf was not easy, and Great Barrier, the nearest settlement, provided a frequent port of call. In January 1968 *Tiri* was wrecked at the entrance to Whangaparapara Harbour, and a replacement vessel, *Tiri II,* ran aground several times during bad weather. Finally, in 1970, after several years of lobbying, the Broadcasting Authority granted Radio Hauraki the first private broadcasting licence in the Auckland region, and after 1,111 days at sea, the pirates finally came ashore. Radio Hauraki is still broadcasting from Auckland.

The pirate radio ship *Tiri II* at its mooring in Colville Channel.

Radio Hauraki

MAORI SITES

E vidence of past Maori settlements on the island can be seen close to every beach and harbour. Some settlements were substantial villages and others merely temporary camps. The villages, many located close to pa, were often laid out on levelled terraces with food-storage pits, cooking ovens and middens; for example, on the lower slopes of Whiritoa at Whangapoua Harbour, and at Harataonga (especially on the cliff edge to the east of the bay). Terraces are clearly visible on the southern slopes of the pa at Awana Beach and on the northern slopes of the Sugar Loaf.

Middens reveal a diet rich in fish and shellfish, and flakes of black obsidian and stone flakes occasionally turn up as well. Obsidian was the most widely used cutting material, and occurs naturally on Great Barrier Island although the best quality obsidian came from Mayor Island. Basalt and greywacke flakes, discarded during the making or sharpening of stone adzes, also turn up. Some middens are very obvious because of the large quantity of shell present. Many occur near beaches, and walking tracks often cut through them, such as the track to Kiwiriki or the track around Whangaparapara Harbour to the old whaling station. The greatest concentration of middens is on the sandspit at Whangapoua.

Every permanent settlement had kumara gardens. These are most apparent where they consist of earth mounds, ditches and drains, stone walls and piles of cleared rock. Stone piles and low walls can be seen on the old consolidated dune of the Whangapoua sandspit. Stone walls and drains occur near Palmers Beach, around Oruawharo (Medlands Beach), at Cape Barrier and on Rakitu and Flat Islands. On the hillside above Fitzroy House, stone lines are clearly visible, perhaps marking boundaries between individual garden plots.

At least 32 Maori pa have been recorded on the island. These fortified sites, with defensive ditches and banks, are located all around Aotea and Rakitu Islands, except on the very inaccessible northern coasts. One of the most impressive pa is on the northern point of Awana Bay. Its southern side was defended by three deep ditches with earthen banks, on which palisades, two to three metres high, would have been built. The rocky cliffs to the north were sufficiently steep to protect the pa without additional defences.

The site of another impressive pa at Tapuwai Point is still clearly visible from the beach. Whiritoa Pa, at the entrance to Whangapoua Harbour, commands a magnificent view along the coast and out to Rakitu. This site has great traditional significance to Ngati Wai because of battles fought here in the late 1700s. At Whangaparapara there were once pa on Lighthouse Point and on the headland above the old whaling station. The track from the head of the bay to the whaling station crosses two pa as well as some small undefended sites and middens. The road to the wharf

Awana Pa.
David Barker

at Blind Bay cuts through a very large pa that ran along the ridge for at least 300 metres. The pa site on the headland between Kaitoke and Medlands Beaches contains stone-faced terraces built to provide living space, and there are also many pits in which kumara and other produce were stored.

There are two pa sites at Tryphena — one on Millers Hill and the other on Pah Point where, despite much recent modification, the original ditch, terraces and at least one pit and midden can be seen.

The predominantly Maori settlements at Katherine Bay have been occupied for more than two hundred years. Garden sites lie on the bay's northern shores, particularly at Te Roto. During the copper-mining era, Ngati Wai supplied the miners with fresh vegetables from these gardens. A 1917 map shows the Te Roto gardens, which were in use until the 1930s, the clearing and orchard at Oruawharo cultivated by Ihapera Kino and Nehana, and several houses at Motairehe. The quarry, Te Tereti, on the shore of Motairehe, is still in use. Here, blocks of tuff are split off for use as doorsteps or hearths.

In 1900, Pita Kino built his house at Kawa, south of Motairehe, and stored his kumara in a large shed nearby. His woolshed and sheep yards were close to the beach and stream so that stock could be easily held before loading them on to a scow to be taken away.

The first school in Katherine Bay was built at Kawa in 1900. Little more than a tin shed, it was replaced by a modern school in 1924. By 1955 the roll had dwindled to just 12 pupils, and the school closed shortly afterwards. It is at present being converted into a meeting-house and marae. Another marae, at Motairehe, is used regularly.

Pita Kino's house at Kawa, Katherine Bay, built in 1900.

Sue Gray

Ease of access to sites associated with Maori settlement, European colonisation and the industrial, farming and other commercial activities of both peoples varies according to terrain and ownership. Common courtesy suggests seeking permission before going on to private land.

Great Barrier Island's human history dates back some 700 years to when the island and several other places along the North Island's eastern coast were colonised by people from East Polynesia. Little evidence of this early occupation remains today, although two middens containing moa bones and a few recognisably very old artefacts have been found. Forest fires dating from 650 years ago could have been caused by these early colonists clearing land.

The thatched cookhouse for construction workers at an early mining site. The cooks are a Mrs Aikman (left) and her daughter Violet.

NZ Herald

Of more than 600 archaeological sites recorded on the island, 350 relate to Maori and suggest continuous occupation through to the early 1800s, when Europeans arrived. At that point, human endeavour on Great Barrier Island turned to boom-and-bust enterprises, including whaling, timber milling, gum-digging and mining copper, silver and gold. Remnants of these activities can be found all over the island.

After the copper ran out in 1867 some of the mining families stayed on and turned to subsistence farming, but it was Robert Barstow, who had landed on the island in 1854 and ran cattle at Rosalie Bay, who was the earliest known European farmer.

The island revealed further riches in 1892 when silver and gold were discovered by the Sanderson brothers at Sunbeam Creek in the Okupu/Whangaparapara area. A large mining settlement was established at Oroville. But gold and silver mining was to meet the same fate as the copper industry, and by 1920 the mines lay abandoned.

Inside the copper mine, Miners Head. Note the green colour of copper ore on the walls.

Tony Bouzaid

25

EUROPEAN COLONIAL SITES

WHALING

Commercial whaling occurred in the nineteenth century and again during the 1950s. At its peak, in 1839, the crews of 200 ships were whaling around New Zealand. Some called into Great Barrier, and although there was no shore-based whaling station on the island, boats landed at Nagle Cove to render down oil. One of the try-pots was later moved to Karaka Bay and is now in the reserve behind the Port Fitzroy store.

The resurgence of whaling in the 1950s led to a whaling station being built at Whangaparapara and operating from 1956 until 1962, when whaling ceased owing to declining catches. The whales (mostly humpbacks) were rendered down for oil and the bones and remains of the carcass processed into meat meal. The station's administration buildings, storage tanks and accommodation for 30 men were located at nearby Tennis Court Bay; the foundations of the ablution block close to the shore are still evident. The station's buildings have been removed, but the concrete ramp up which the whales were winched and the concrete foundations of the factory are now part of a boat repair yard. Around the point to the west of the whaling factory lie the foundations of the building where the explosives for killing whales were stored.

Whaling station at Whangaparapara in the 1950s.

George Medland

SHIPPING

The earliest known ship to visit Great Barrier Island was the whaling ship *William and Ann*. It was dismasted in 1796, but made it into Tryphena Harbour, where four replacement kauri spars were obtained.

The first ship of many to be built on the island was the barque *Stirlingshire*, built by John Gillies at Nagle Cove between 1841 and 1848 for William Abercrombie, Jeremiah Nagle and William Webster, who were partners in a mining venture (see later). Made of pohutukawa with kauri planking, the ship weighed 409 tonnes and was 33 metres long. Gillies also built the *Tryphena* and the *Rory O'More*. Richard Smith's shipyard at Smiths Bay is the best known. Here, Smith built schooners and cutters between 1873 and 1880, including the *Atlanta* and the *Florence*.

Graves of some of the victims of the *Wairarapa* shipwreck.

DOC

Great Barrier Island has been the scene of more than 30 shipwrecks, the best known being the SS *Wairarapa*. On 29 October 1894, she struck the cliffs near Miners Head, resulting in the loss of 121 lives — the third worst shipping disaster in New Zealand history. Exactly a hundred years later, a plaque was unveiled at the point where the ship struck.

Another famous shipwreck at Great Barrier Island was the *Wiltshire*. This 7,800-tonne steamer struck the east coast

near Rosalie Bay in May 1922. In a sensational rescue that took two days, the crew of 103 was rescued by breeches buoy (an endless rope loop slung between the ship and the shore). Today both these wreck sites are popular with recreational divers.

Top: A diver visits the *Wairarapa* wreck site off Miners Head. Although much broken up by explosives used during salvage operations, this wreck remains an interesting and popular diving site.

Roger Grace

Above: The broken wreck of the *Wiltshire* a few days after she struck the eastern coast in 1922.

MINING

Copper was discovered at Miners Head in 1841. The following year Abercrombie, Nagle and Webster started New Zealand's first mining operation there, and a village was established in the valley at Miners Bay. By 1845 the mine was employing up to 40 people. However, the easily accessible copper soon ran out and the last mine closed in 1867.

Mining tunnels are still clearly visible in the Miners Head area, although the only access is by water. The earliest workings were about 60 metres above sea level on the north-facing cliffs. However, in 1845 mining ceased and the people left the island for Auckland because of the threat of hostilities between Maori and Pakeha in the far north.

The next copper-mining venture was run by Theophilus

Heale and Frederick Whitaker from 1855 to 1859. They concentrated on the south-facing cliffs of Miners Head and installed a crusher, steam engine and workshops on the beach. The Great Barrier Land Harbour and Mining Company carried out the final major mining venture from 1861 to 1866. The principal shareholders were Heale, Henry Govett, a resident of Taranaki, and a Major Rocke of Her Majesty's Navy. They installed better extraction machinery but the operation soon became uneconomic. The remains of the engine house built in 1851 still stand on the shore, although little is left of the breakwater or crushing floor. The miners lived in an adjacent bay and walked around the headland to the mine, but little remains of their dwellings today. In total the copper-mining era on the island yielded about 2,500 tonnes of ore.

In 1892, brothers Ben and William Sanderson discovered silver ore, containing also a little gold, on the southern slopes of Te Ahumata. Several companies took out mining licences, but none of these ventures lasted long. By 1933 the Te Ahumata mines had yielded over 1,300 kg of silver-gold bullion, mostly from the Barrier Reefs claim.

The Oroville stamping battery photographed just after its construction in 1900. The Barrier Reefs Gold Mining Company lasted only two years in business.

Auckland War Memorial Museum

The first of these mines was the Sunbeam, on the banks of Sunbeam Creek, where the remains of the boiler, iron chimney, two fireplaces for the furnaces and two settling ponds are still present. In 1900 the Barrier Reefs Gold Mining Company built a 20-stamp battery mill at Oroville (sometimes spelt Oreville). This company closed after just two years, but mining was carried on spasmodically until 1920, when the battery was removed. The stone wall that held part of the battery is still evident alongside the Whangaparapara Road. Nearby, above the road, is a terrace where the manager's office was built. Tunnels and the remains of the concrete foundations for the steam engine, tram tracks and a water race also are nearby.

South of Oroville are the remains of the third major mine on the island, Iona, and its five-stamp battery, built in 1901. The crushed ore was taken to Oroville for processing. All that remains today are some concrete slabs and mounting bolts.

TIMBER

In addition to mining copper, the Great Barrier Land Harbour and Mining Company logged kauri in the Kaiarara, Wairahi and Kiwiriki catchments from 1862 until 1867 and milled it at Bush's Beach. During 1865, the *Southern Cross* newspaper estimated their mill to be the largest in New Zealand. When the company went bankrupt, the receiver removed the mill and machinery. Only the sills of the dams on the Kaiarara South Fork remain, although terraces and levelled areas around the creek mouth at Bushs Beach

An old steam traction engine forms part of the picturesque remains from the logging era at the old Whangaparapara timber mill site.

DOC

WHANGAPARA
GT BARRIER 2300D

indicate the probable location of the mill. The mill manager lived across the bay on a promontory now known as Blairs Landing. Grapevines and spring bulbs are all that is left to indicate his house site.

Easily accessible kauri was logged by small operators until 1888, when much of the land now administered by DOC as forest was purchased by the Kauri Timber Company, which leased out timber-cutting rights around Palmers Bush and Coopers Castle. Felled trees were hauled out by bullock teams. Some logs were taken to Harataonga and floated out to waiting scows. At Whangapoua the logs were held in the Whangapoua Stream in booms and then loaded on to scows.

Exports from the island were not subject to customs duty before the First World War, providing an incentive to process and export timber logged in other areas. Accordingly, in 1909 the Kauri Timber Company built a mill at Whangaparapara to process kauri rafted out from the mainland; it did not log timber on the island until much later. The mill employed 50 men at the time of opening and was reputed to be the largest in the southern hemisphere.

The Kauri Timber Company mill at Whangaparapara, early last century. Logs were hauled up the slipway at centre and sawn timber was loaded from the wharf with the two ships lying alongside. The wharf piles and other remnants are still visible today.

Matakohe Museum

Log booms at Whangaparapara
in the early 1900s

Matakohe Museum

In 1914 it closed as the outbreak of war resulted in a labour shortage and lack of demand for timber. The mill was set by the water's edge, and its wharf was 275 metres long. The mill had a double-cutting bandsaw, gang-edger and two drag benches, all powered by steam produced by four boilers. Many of the wharf piles and remains of railway tracks and some machinery are still clearly visible in the bay at low tide. At the mill site, the sawdust reclamation along the shoreline can be seen, and an old engine used to shift logs. Also visible are the remains of the chimney-stack and a concrete block that held one of the saws. A small village housing 50 workers and their families was built close by, along with the school, hall and library; and tennis courts were sited in the adjacent bay. After milling ceased, the buildings were removed, many being taken to other parts of the island for use as houses or holiday homes, for example the cottage behind Fitzroy House.

From 1926 to 1940 the Kauri Timber Company

concentrated on stands of kauri that previously had been considered inaccessible. Dams were built on small streams and the logs piled up behind them. The dams were then tripped, flushing the logs out to the coast. Two of the large dams on the Kaiarara Stream, built in 1926, can still be seen. On the eastern side of the island a tramway was constructed, enabling cut logs to be transported by steam haulers to Whangaparapara. This tramline is now used as a tramping track, running from Aotea Road to Whangaparapara and close to the hot springs.

At Whangaparapara there was a large camp with quarters for married and single men, a hall, school, post office and store. During the working week, the men lived close to their work in small camps. At first they lived in bunkhouses with a resident cook in charge of the cook-house and dining hall; later they lodged in small huts, two men per hut. Today, the only reminders of their occupation are lines marking out the sites of gardens, some trees and plants and the foundations of the butcher's shop.

Kauri logging on Great Barrier in the 1930s. An extensive network of bush tramways like this enabled timber extraction over a wide area. Today, the tramway routes form the basis of many walking tracks.

NZ Herald

KAURI GUM

Kauri gum was collected from the 1860s, but never on as large a scale as in Northland. By 1889 between 40 and 50 gum-diggers were working on the island. It is likely that they excavated and created the hot bath at Peach Tree Hot Springs. By 1916, few were left.

COLONIAL HOMES AND COMMERCIAL PREMISES

Robert Barstow, the island's first farmer, arrived in 1854 and ran cattle at Rosalie Bay. Five years later, he sold the land to Neil and Emily Malcolm. In the northern half of the island, John and Susan Moor began farming at Mohunga in 1859, and two years later the Flinn family (William and Charlotte, their children and William's brother Peter) took up farming on the Wairahi Estuary. The only remaining traces of their homes are the stone walls at Mohunga, built by the Moors.

When the copper mining company went into liquidation in 1868, land was given to some miners in lieu of wages owed. Edward Paddison at Karaka Bay, brothers William and Alfred Edlington at Tapuwai and George Stark at Whangapoua all received land, but none of their houses still stands.

Opposite the wharf at Port Fitzroy is one of the oldest houses left standing on the island. Fitzroy House, originally called Glenfern, was built by Reg Cooper in 1901. The years

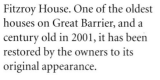

Fitzroy House. One of the oldest houses on Great Barrier, and a century old in 2001, it has been restored by the owners to its original appearance.

Fullers

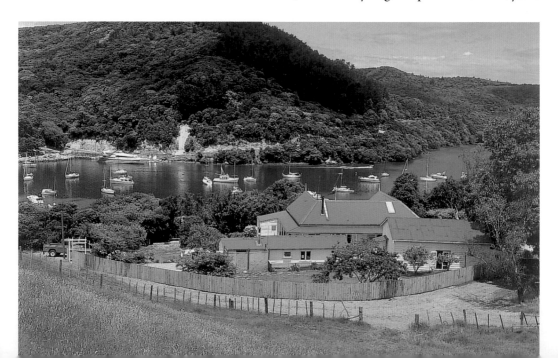

since have seen many additions and alterations. The house's present owners, Tony and Mal Bouzaid, have restored it to its original appearance.

Two other dwellings at Port Fitzroy include Le Roy House and Le Roy Cottage. Emileus Le Roy built the original house in about 1880. This burnt down and was replaced in 1902; the second house was demolished in 1989. A third house was built that same year, close to the site of the first two. Le Roy Cottage, which is still standing, was built by Emileus's son, Emileus George, right on the shores of the harbour sometime after 1900. One of the last members of the Le Roy family on the island, Girlie, is buried on the headland between Rarohara and Kaiarara. She died in 1979. Many other early Port Fitzroy settlers are buried on Quoin (or Grave) Island.

This stone wall at Raohara, Port Fitzroy, was built for scows to unload at after they had been beached on the high tide. It has survived since the 1890s.

Tony Bouzaid

In the 1890s John Warren built the stone wall on the foreshore at Rarohara, Port Fitzroy. Scows could sail right up to it at high tide for ease of loading and unloading. The stone walls built by Dr Hallen at a small inlet on the southern shores of Kaiarara Bay are also in excellent condition. The walls and associated bakery were built about 1910. It is thought that Hallen, a doctor, also ran the bakery.

Port Fitzroy School opened in 1924, but in the mid-1930s, with only eight or nine pupils left, it closed and the building was used as the local hall. During the Second

The army camp at Port Fitzroy, 1945.

Garth Cooper Collection

World War it was used as an officers' mess for Battle Station Great Barrier that was located at Port Fitzroy. The building is now the Port Fitzroy Boating Club house. The army built an ablution block and the Salvation Army entertainment centre as well as several small buildings, but only the foundations of these buildings remain.

Across the island from Port Fitzroy, Whangapoua Harbour was the scene of much activity during the early years of colonisation, although few early buildings are left. At Tapuwai, the original Edlington family house is long gone, but the honey house, dating back to 1918, is still in good condition and is used regularly by the Mabey family for functions. At Tapuwai Point is the small cemetery containing the bodies of some of those lost when the SS *Wairarapa* sank. Another cemetery is located on the foreshore at Kawa.

At the mouth of Whangapoua Creek the homestead built in 1900 by William and Amy Sanderson still stands. William was the son of the first Sanderson (also a William) to come to the island. The dairy, foundation posts of the woolshed and some trees from the original orchard also can be seen. In the creek close to the house are logs with chains attached, sunk deep into the tidal mud, used to hold the logs in booms. On the western side of the sandspit at

Whangapoua timber was also held in a boom, chained to an anchor which is now located on the foreshore behind the Port Fitzroy store.

Left: The Alcock house at Harataonga, built in 1906.
DOC

Below: Tom Medland's wash-house, built about 1894.
Brenda Sewell

South of Whangapoua, at Harataonga, stands the Alcock house, built in 1906. William and Sarah Alcock were the first European settlers at Harataonga, and this house was built to replace their first home, which had been built in 1884. The subsequent house has been extensively altered inside but outwardly has changed little. The family's graves are on the hill near the house.

At Kaitoke, further south again, the oldest house is another Sanderson family homestead. It has been much altered since it was first built about 1920. The Gray homestead at Kaitoke was also built a little after this time, but is no longer occupied and is derelict.

Tom Medland, who first worked on Great Barrier Island as a farm labourer from 1866 to 1869, returned in 1880 and built a two-roomed whare near the beach at Medlands Beach. He and his family lived there until he built their homestead, Woolstone, in 1894. This home has since been demolished, but the sawmill/woolshed, wash-house and cream store are still in good condition. The wash-house and cream store were moved closer to the beach in the late 1980s and around 1994 respectively, and the two buildings now contain the Benson museum of Medland artefacts. Mrs Benson is a grand-daughter of the original Medland family.

St John's Community Church,
Medlands.

Don Armitage

St John's Community Church at Medlands Beach is the only consecrated church on Great Barrier Island. Built of kauri at Awanui, near Kaitaia, in 1923, it was barged to the island in 1986 and re-dedicated in November of that year.

At the entrance to Whangapoua Harbour are the remains of the beacon erected in 1909 to guide ships into the harbour. The walk at low tide along the western shoreline passes several historic sites, including a 1930s logging camp and a timber mill dating from 1910. Nearby, ridges from various garden plots can be seen, and the concrete slab close to the water is the remains of Roy Gibbons's butcher shop. In the next bay are the remains of the mill and associated village. Tennis Court Bay takes its name from the tennis courts from the mill days. At Whangaparapara itself, on the shore opposite the site of the mill and whaling factory, is the building now known as Great Barrier Lodge. The lodge, originally the mill manager's house, was shifted across the harbour to its present site in the 1920s.

The Sanderson family mentioned earlier first settled on Great Barrier at Blind Bay, south of Whangaparapara Harbour, in 1863. Their stone dairy is the only building remaining from this early period. Between 1900 and 1910, Toby Sanderson built another house in the bay to the east of the wharf. The house still stands, although somewhat altered. At Allom Bay

Rose Cottage, at Puriri Bay, dates
from about the late 1860s.

DOC

the remains of the chimney of Tom Ryan's house is the only reminder that a house once stood here.

Settlement of Tryphena Bay began in the mid-1860s, and Ox Park, built by George Blackwell in 1870, is the oldest house still standing on Great Barrier Island. An upper storey was added in 1880. The houses built about 1900 by two of the Blackwell sons are still occupied. Jonathan Blackwell built Pohutukawa Lodge, behind which is the old cream store

and dairy (now used as a bunkhouse for backpackers). His brother Tom built Tryphena House at Mulberry Grove. At Puriri Bay the small cottage (sometimes known as Rose Cottage) built by Tommy Alcock probably dates to the late 1860s or early 1870s.

There are four cemeteries at Tryphena: one at Puriri Bay, with principally Blair family graves; one close by, with Bailey and Alcock graves, and two cemeteries at Gooseberry Flat. The older of these two contains mainly Blackwell graves. Tryphena School was built in 1884 and moved 50 metres in 1973 to its present site. It is now used as a community hall.

Above: Tryphena School in its early days. The building is still clearly recognisable (top)

Auckland War Memorial Museum

The outer islands of the Hauraki Gulf — the Poor Knights, Hen and Chickens, Mokohinaus, and Great Barrier — once formed part of a major volcanic chain that stretched from eastern Northland to the Bay of Plenty.

Great Barrier is of particular geological interest because of its size, wide variety of rocks, and extensive coastal exposures. Studies over the past 130 years have shown that while the island's rock formations are remarkably similar to those of Coromandel Peninsula in composition and age, there are some important differences. Recent dating of the rocks has indicated, for example, that volcanism ceased much earlier on Great Barrier.

The geology also has played an important role in the island's human history and economy. Local obsidian (volcanic glass) was widely utilised by the early Maori inhabitants of Aotea, and hard volcanic rocks are used today in roading and construction. During the mid to late nineteenth century, significant mineral deposits were discovered, which subsequently led to small-scale mining operations in northern and central parts of Great Barrier (see p.23 and 28). Nowadays, geological features such as the Kaitoke hot springs and the spectacular pinnacles and bluffs of the Mt Hobson (Hirakimata) area are among the island's more popular natural attractions.

THE OLDEST ROCKS

Although Great Barrier is essentially volcanic in origin, ancient sedimentary rocks underlie the entire island. These rocks form the northern part of the island (Te Paparahi block) and also outcrop around Harataonga. They consist mainly of hard, grey sandstone and mudstone, but also include some conglomerate. The sandstone is largely composed of small fragments of volcanic rock, and forms distinct layers alternating with beds of mudstone. In places, these layered rocks have been so severely deformed that it is difficult to discern their original sedimentary character.

Fossils are extremely rare, although a few belemnites — the hard parts of extinct squids — have been found in the northern block and at Harataonga. These indicate that the sandstone and mudstone were deposited during the Jurassic Period, about 150 million years ago, in a deep marine trough off the eastern coast of the supercontinent of Gondwana. Granite boulders in the conglomerate probably came from what is now West Antarctica, or from eastern Australia. Collectively, these ancient sedimentary rocks are commonly referred to as 'greywacke', and make up what is called the 'greywacke basement'.

Later, in the early Cretaceous Period, the greywacke rocks were uplifted to create a new landmass — ancestral New Zealand — which then, about 80 million years ago, separated from Australia and Antarctica and slowly moved eastward. The Tasman Sea formed as the rift between New Zealand and Australia widened.

Small fold in the ancient sedimentary rocks (greywacke) at Harataonga, defined by a layer of sandstone. Such contortions may have been caused by slumping of relatively soft strata on the sea floor 150 million years ago.

Phil Moore

For the next 40 to 50 million years much of the Auckland region, including Great Barrier, apparently remained above sea level, although rivers and streams gradually wore down the land. Eventually, the sea advanced over the northern Coromandel area, and most likely Great Barrier as well, but soon retreated, leaving no record of this event on the island.

VOLCANIC HISTORY

Development of the modern boundary between the Australian and Pacific tectonic plates about 25 million years ago had a dramatic effect on New Zealand. As the westward-moving Pacific plate started sliding beneath the Australian plate, volcanoes erupted progressively to form two chains, one on each side of Northland. The eastern volcanic chain extended from Whangaroa through Whangarei and Great Barrier to the Coromandel area, where the earliest eruptions began around 18 million years ago.

On what is now Great Barrier, molten magma migrated up through the greywacke basement between 16 and 18 million years ago to form a series of volcanic dikes. Some of these dikes are up to 30 metres wide and more than a kilometre long. They are particularly conspicuous in the

Volcanic dike, Harataonga.
Phil Moore

Dark greywacke transected by much younger, lighter-coloured volcanic dikes near Miners Head.
Phil Moore

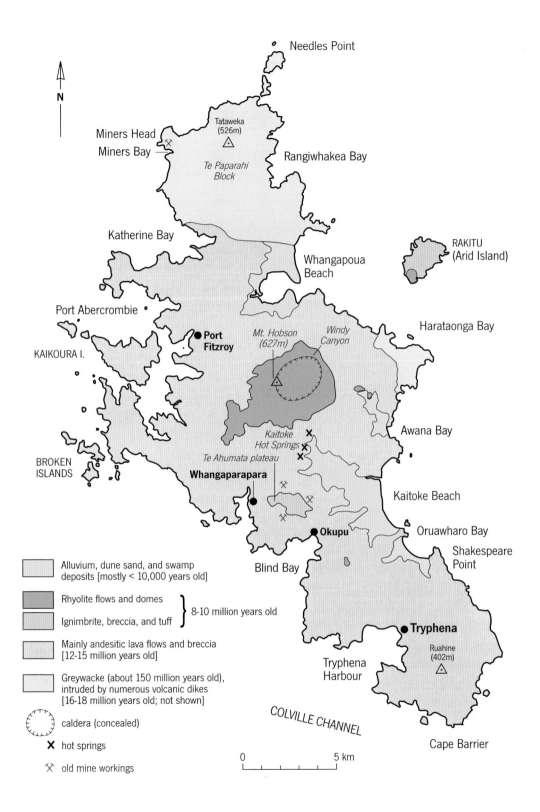

Needles Point

N

Tataweka
(526m)

Miners Head
Miners Bay

Te Paparahi
Block

Rangiwhakea Bay

Katherine Bay

Whangapoua
Beach

RAKITU
(Arid Island)

Port Abercrombie

Harataonga Bay

KAIKOURA I.

Port
Fitzroy

Mt. Hobson
(627m)

Windy
Canyon

Awana Bay

BROKEN
ISLANDS

Kaitoke
Hot Springs

Te Ahumata plateau

Whangaparapara

Kaitoke Beach

Okupu

Oruawharo Bay

Blind Bay

Shakespeare
Point

Alluvium, dune sand, and swamp
deposits [mostly < 10,000 years old]

Rhyolite flows and domes

Ignimbrite, breccia, and tuff

} 8-10 million years old

Mainly andesitic lava flows and breccia
[12-15 million years old]

Greywacke (about 150 million years old),
intruded by numerous volcanic dikes
[16-18 million years old; not shown]

caldera (concealed)

✕ hot springs

✗ old mine workings

Tryphena

Ruahine
(402m)

Tryphena
Harbour

COLVILLE CHANNEL

0   5 km

Cape Barrier

A simplified geological map of Great Barrier Island.

high cliffs along the rugged northern coast between Miners Bay and Needles Point, but are common as far south as Harataonga. Some of the dikes may have reached the surface and fed small volcanoes, but if so no trace of the volcanoes remains today. Geologists have been unable to locate the source of these dikes, but they must have originated from a large magma chamber lying several kilometres below the surface.

Intrusion of the dikes was followed by a major period of volcanism. This produced a very thick sequence of volcanic rocks that now makes up the bulk of Great Barrier, including Rakitu (Arid Island) and other outlying islands. These rocks probably are up to two kilometres thick beneath Great Barrier, and also continue well offshore.

The older parts of this volcanic sequence consist of rubbly volcanic breccias, lava flows and deposits of tuff (rock made up of consolidated ash), and are predominantly andesitic in composition. These rocks formed the broad flanks of a large volcanic cone, probably centred some 5 to

Coarse andesitic breccia and layered tuff (centre) on Motutaiko, Broken Islands. These rocks were deposited, probably by mudflows and transient streams, on the eastern flank of the massive West Barrier Volcano 12-15 million years ago.

Phil Moore

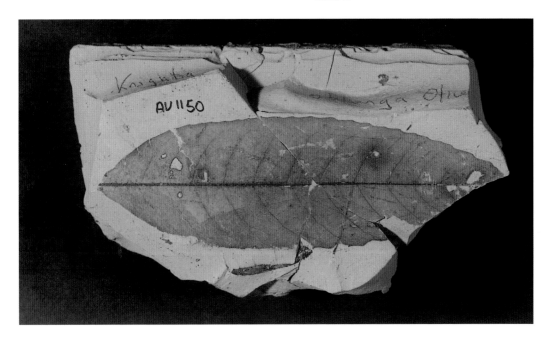

10 kilometres west of the present coast, near Horn Rock. This volcano — termed the 'West Barrier Volcano' — was of a similar type to Mts Ruapehu and Taranaki (Egmont) in the North Island, and perhaps similar in size. There may also have been some smaller 'parasitic' cones situated on the outer flanks of the main volcano.

The dating of two lava flows near Whangaparapara suggests that the West Barrier Volcano was active 12 to 14 million years ago. Pollen and spores from old lake sediments within the volcanic sequence south of Oruawharo Bay provide a similar age. Leaf impressions, freshwater mussel shells and petrified wood have also been found in a few places. These fossils clearly show that the volcano erupted on land, even though the sea level at that time is thought to have been considerably higher than now.

The major cone-building andesitic eruptions were succeeded by volcanic activity of a very different character. During this phase the eruptions produced lighter-coloured and more silica-rich rhyolite, ignimbrite (a rock composed of pumice and ash), breccia and ash, mainly in the Rakitu and Mt Hobson areas. By then, the sea level had fallen significantly, and the shoreline apparently lay well to the east.

Fossil leaf from lake sediments (12 to 13 million years old) within the volcanic sequence near Oruawharo Bay. Length about 10 cm.

Geology Dept., University of Auckland

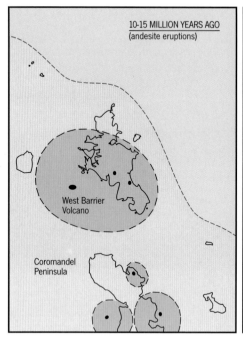

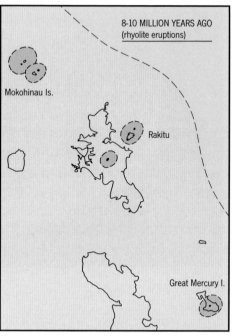

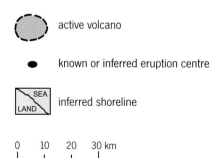

Geography of the Great Barrier
area at various times in the past.

At Windy Canyon, prolonged erosion by rain and running water has created a remarkable rocky landscape. The prominent spines and bluffs are composed of obsidian breccia, an unusual rock type made up of volcanic glass (obsidian) fragments. This breccia apparently developed through sudden chilling and extensive fracturing of lava around the margin of the large rhyolite dome formed by eruptions in the Mt Hobson area some 8 to 9 million years ago.

Phil Moore

Rakitu is the eroded remnant of a complex rhyolite volcano. The cliffs show old rhyolite lava buried beneath ignimbrite, breccia, ash and lava flows, which probably erupted from vents nearby. Rhyolite also forms a dome structure at the southern end of the island. A basalt lava flow on an islet just offshore from Rakitu is of particular geological interest as it represents the only known basalt in the Great Barrier area.

The Mt Hobson area consists largely of rhyolite lava and obsidian breccia, which were apparently erupted from vents in a large caldera (collapse crater) about eight to nine million years ago. (Most of the obsidian used by Maori, however, was obtained from Te Ahumata, where it was of better quality.) These rhyolitic rocks have been deeply eroded, in places forming spectacular pinnacles and bluffs; for example, at Windy Canyon. Although the semi-circular caldera is no longer visible, geophysical studies indicate that it had a diameter of two and a half to three kilometres, and that its floor now lies some two kilometres below the surface.

Explosive eruptions associated with the formation of the Mt Hobson caldera may have produced thick ignimbrite deposits that covered most of Great Barrier. The Te Ahumata plateau, situated six kilometres south of Mt Hobson, is perhaps the only surviving remnant of those deposits. Its prominent bluffs (for example, Whitecliffs) are composed of ignimbrite and tuff, beneath which are about 30 metres of coarse sedimentary rocks. These include thin mudstone layers which were obviously deposited in a lake environment, as they contain well-preserved leaf impressions (see p.45) and freshwater mussel shells.

Later, the ignimbrite, tuff and lake sediments forming what is now the Te Ahumata plateau were hardened (silicified) as a result of hot, silica-rich waters percolating through the rocks. Mineralised quartz veins which formed about the same time probably acted as channels for hot water to migrate to the surface, where silica sinter was deposited.

Volcanic eruptions apparently ceased at least four to five million years ago, but sufficient heat is still being generated beneath the island for hot water to reach the surface north of Te Ahumata.

Banded silver-bearing ore from the Iona Mine, Te Ahumata. This sample contains the equivalent of about 250 g silver per tonne.

Geology Dept,
University of Auckland

Malachite, one of the ores of copper, from Miners Head.

Geology Dept,
University of Auckland

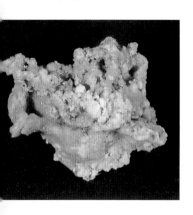

MINERALS AND HOT SPRINGS

A wide variety of minerals have been found on Great Barrier, including copper- and silver-bearing ores. Copper was discovered at Miners Head in the late 1830s, and mined from 1842 to 1867 (see p.23 and 28). The main lode at Miners Head is up to 12 metres thick, and consists of shattered rock with pockets of chalcopyrite (copper iron sulphide) and pyrite (iron sulphide). Lead, zinc, gold and silver are also present in small quantities. Colourful green to blue copper sulphates and carbonates adorn the walls of the large mine chamber, and form conspicuous stains on cliff faces around the headland.

The discovery in 1892 of silver-bearing ore at Te Ahumata led to the development of three main mines in the area (see p.29). The silver, along with small quantities of gold, was obtained from narrow quartz veins containing various sulphide minerals, in particular pyrargyrite (silver antimony sulphide). More recent sampling has revealed ore grades as high as 1,470 g/tonne silver and 9 g/tonne gold, with ratios of silver to gold ranging from about 30:1 to 100:1. Other minerals identified in the ore include stibnite (antimony sulphide), sulphides of arsenic, and chalcopyrite.

These minerals were deposited (from mineralised fluids) at temperatures of between 160°C and 270°C, and depths of around 100 to 300 metres below ground level. The present surface of Te Ahumata plateau, therefore, is probably only slightly lower than the original land surface that existed at the time the quartz veins were formed, more than five million years ago.

Europeans first 'discovered' the thermal springs in the Kaitoke Valley in the 1860s, although they had apparently long been used by local Maori. The hottest of these springs reaches 84°C, and the waters contain high levels of sodium chloride (salt), potassium and calcium. Some of them also give off minor amounts of gas, mostly nitrogen, carbon dioxide and methane.

All of the springs are situated along the western margin of the Kaitoke Swamp, and it seems likely that hot water rises up along a concealed fault in the vicinity. The source of the spring waters is believed to be a large reservoir deep beneath the island, possibly hotter than 250°C, although the waters cool as they slowly migrate towards the surface. The spring water is essentially deep-circulating groundwater enriched by chemicals leaching from hot volcanic rocks surrounding the main reservoir. The gases, however, may be generated from organic matter in the greywacke basement rocks several kilometres below the surface.

The Kaitoke hot springs have an unusually high silver content, which has led to the suggestion that they may represent a continuation of the thermal activity responsible for forming the silver-bearing quartz veins of Te Ahumata. If so, then the geothermal system beneath Great Barrier has been in existence for well over five million years.

THE LAST TWO MILLION YEARS

Since the beginning of the Ice Age, about two million years ago, there have been at least 30 separate glaciations (cold periods), interspersed with brief periods of relatively warm climate similar to that of today. Each cold/warm cycle has lasted for 40 to a 100,000 years. During the glacial periods the sea level probably fell by more than a hundred metres. The Colville Channel, which now separates the island from Coromandel Peninsula, is only about 50 metres deep, although beneath it lies a considerable thickness of sediments of unknown age. It is not clear when the Colville Channel was first formed, but we do know that at the peak of the last glacial period, approximately 18,000 years ago,

The Broken Islands (foreground), off the western coast of Great Barrier. During the dramatic rise in sea level following the last glaciation, about 18,000 years ago, valleys were drowned and hills were transformed into islands.

Brent Baker

the sea level was about 120 metres lower, and then rose to its present level by around 6,500 years ago. It therefore is reasonably certain that Great Barrier has been an island for at least the past 10,000 years.

The modern landscape of Great Barrier is, for the most part, a legacy of the Ice Age. When the sea level was lower, rivers and streams would have carved out larger valleys, and erosion increased because there was less forest cover. During the last two million years the hills have been worn down by perhaps hundreds of metres, and apart from Te Ahumata plateau, little now remains of the previous land surface.

As the sea level rose after the last glacial period, valley systems were drowned to form Great Barrier's indented coastline (notably around Port Fitzroy) and the numerous outlying islands. The process of erosion slowed down and sediments began to fill the drowned valleys, particularly on the more exposed eastern coast, where sand spits and barrier beaches built up across the open bays. Swamps have since developed behind many of the eastern beaches, the largest of which now occupies the lower Kaitoke Valley.

The nature of the rocks has also had a considerable influence on the landscape. In the northern (Te Paparahi) block, for example, the drainage pattern is partly controlled by fractures in the sedimentary rocks, and harder sandstone and dike rocks form many of the coastal promontories. Elsewhere on the island many of the more prominent landforms are made up of less easily eroded rocks, like the peaks of Mt Hobson and nearby Mt Heale, which are composed of rhyolite lava.

Great Barrier is still evolving, and as erosion cuts deeper into the land, older rocks are exposed. These may eventually yield new information to add to the story of the island's ancient past.

CHAPTER FOUR

MAJOR ECOSYSTEMS

A flight over Great Barrier reveals two of its main features: the rugged, forested backbone punctuated by dramatic rock outcrops, and the contrast between the western and eastern coastlines. The island is indeed a barrier, with open surf beaches confronting the Pacific breakers, and sheltered fiord-like inlets and harbours facing the Hauraki Gulf.

This landscape encompasses 10 major habitat types or ecosystems, which from the air can be taken in by the discerning eye within a few minutes, but a broader appreciation obviously requires more time on the ground. These ecosystems approximately correspond to 10 'land units' defined by the Auckland City Council (see below).

Map of part of the Awana area, showing the main 'Land Units' in sequence from the coast to the mountain summits. This arrangement of vegetation types, associated with topography and altitude, is commonly repeated elsewhere on Great Barrier.
Key:
Land Unit (LU) 1, coastal cliffs.
LU 2, dune systems and sand flats.
LU 3, alluvial flats.
LU 4, wetlands.
LU 5, foothills and lower slopes.
LU 6, steep pastured slopes.
LU 7, steep infertile coastal slopes (here included in 6).
LU 8, regenerating slopes with tea-tree scrub.
LU 9, low fertility hills (here included within 8 owing to similar tea-tree cover)
LU 10, forest.

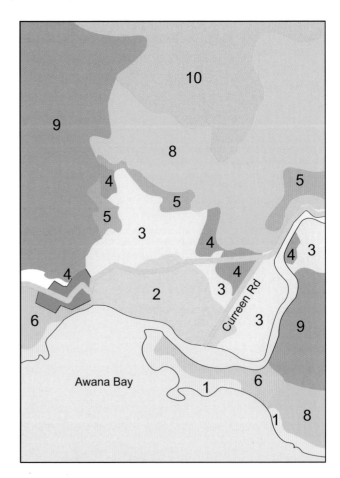

ECOSYSTEM TERMINOLOGY

The term **ecosystem** as used here applies to the vegetation and its associated birds, reptiles, amphibians and invertebrates in a particular area. An ecosystem is a dynamic entity, with nutrients cycling from the soil into the plants, and photosynthetic energy flowing from plants to higher levels in the food web (insects, birds, and so on). The vegetation forms the habitat for these different organisms, and the species change as the vegetation varies over the landscape. This chapter deals mainly with the vegetation cover, as birds and other organisms are covered in other chapters.

Boundaries of ecosystems are not well defined, as natural vegetation transitions tend to merge gradually into one another. Also, most vegetation changes in composition over time, especially in places like Great Barrier Island, where much of the original forest has been burned or logged.

The subsequent process of regeneration is **succession**. This refers to any gradual change in composition; for example, when scrub and then forest trees take over farmland that has been abandoned. Thus, changes occur within systems and the difference between one type of vegetation and another may be only a function of time.

Consequently, to describe the ecosystems of an area, we need to identify the physical boundaries or groupings of vegetation on a map, and to have an understanding of succession through time. The **land units** that the Auckland City Council uses in its district plan are related to topography, drainage and current land use or successional stage, so they comprise distinctive ecosystems and are useful to describe the ecosystems outlined opposite.

Sand-binding plants on Kaitoke Beach. In the background there is a tuft of marram grass (*Ammophila arenaria*), and pingao (*Desmoschoenus spiralis*) at right. The middle distance is occupied by *Spinifex sericeus* and the foreground by the sedge *Carex pumila*.

John Ogden

The vegetation of Great Barrier Island has many similarities with that of the Coromandel Peninsula, and together they comprise a distinctive geological and botanical region. There are also links to the wider kauri forest region of Northland.

On Great Barrier itself, notable differences in plant distribution occur between the island's southern, central and northern blocks. These patterns point to former land connections, but the island also has some endemic plants, which suggests prolonged periods of isolation. Indeed, over the past half-million years a number of glacial periods caused ice to build up on the world's landmasses so the sea level dropped, creating a lowland plain across much of the present Hauraki Gulf and connecting the island to the mainland. In the intervening warmer periods rising sea levels again isolated the island, as at present (see map, p.46).

Before the arrival of humans, the natural vegetation cover of most of Great Barrier was forest from sea level to mountain top. The only exceptions were areas of swamp or sand dune, but even these had some distinctive forests of their own. Natural disturbances, such as storms or occasional lightning-induced fires, initiated regeneration of the forest, often with manuka (*Leptospermum scoparium*) and kanuka (*Kunzea ericoides*) important as colonising species.

The forest composition varied according to soil type, drainage, proximity to the coast, time since last disturbance, topography, aspect and altitude. Because so much of the original forest has now gone, it is hard to put together the pieces of this three-dimensional puzzle, but the distinctive coastal fringe and the changes of vegetation associated with altitude and topography can still be seen; for example, on the walk up Mt Hobson (Hirakimata) from Kiarara Bay.

RECENT COASTAL ECOSYSTEMS

The dune systems, wetlands (swamps and estuaries) and alluvial flats (land units 2, 3 and 4, respectively) of eastern Great Barrier are linked in origin. Although each has its own distinctive collection of species, these three sea-level ecosystems are strongly interdependent, implying that they should be managed as a whole. For example, draining the swamps behind the dunes for farmland in the past must have lowered the water-table between them and the sea, reducing the amount of fresh water beneath the dunes so that sand-dune vegetation died and the dunes became mobile again. (Who knows what influence it also had on intertidal shellfish beds on the sandy beaches beyond the dunes?)

Major natural ecosystems of Eastern Great Barrier Island. The coastal aggradational ecosystems, dunes, estuaries and swamps are much more restricted on the western side of the island, where instead there are deep water bays with steep surroundings.

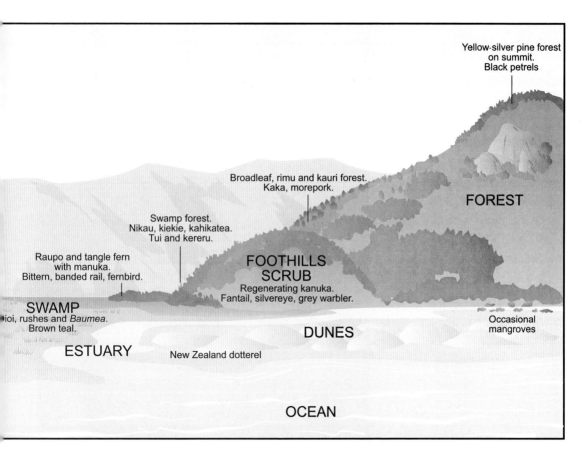

Yellow-silver pine forest on summit. Black petrels

FOREST

Broadleaf, rimu and kauri forest. Kaka, morepork.

Swamp forest. Nikau, kiekie, kahikatea. Tui and kereru.

Raupo and tangle fern with manuka. Bittern, banded rail, fernbird.

FOOTHILLS SCRUB
Regenerating kanuka. Fantail, silvereye, grey warbler.

SWAMP
ioi, rushes and *Baumea*. Brown teal.

ESTUARY

New Zealand dotterel

DUNES

Occasional mangroves

OCEAN

These habitats were formed after the sea reached its present level about six thousand years ago. Sand bars spread across the larger bays (Medlands, Kaitoke, Awana and Whangapoua), creating estuaries and lagoons. As the coastal dunes built up, the lagoons gradually escaped the influence of the tide. Sediment from the surrounding hills and peat from dead vegetation converted the lagoons into freshwater swamps, such as Kaitoke Swamp. Drainage of the swamps created the coastal flats.

Beds of cockles and traces of mangrove pollen buried in Kaitoke Swamp indicate that salt water used to reach some three kilometres in from the present beach. Marine deposits also underlie some of the Awana flats. At Awana, the Claris–Fitzroy road, skirting the former swamp, now divides the seaward dune system from the alluvial flats. The flats have shrunk downwards by at least a metre since being drained in the 1940s.

DUNE SYSTEMS

Mobile coastal dunes, constantly shaped by wind-blown sand and with little vegetation cover to stabilise them, generally seem to date from after European arrival. Beneath

Close-up of flowers of pingao
(*Desmoschoenus spiralis*).

Len Doel

these dunes lie remnants of ancient soil surfaces containing burned-over soil and shells. This can be seen where the Awana Stream has eroded the dunes opposite the pa at Awana, and indicates that the dunes were forest or scrub-covered in early Maori times. Dune ridges, formed parallel to the shore, tend to be blown inland. On the low areas between dunes, the dry upper sand is blown away, eroding down to the level of the water-table. Most of the island's dune systems are essentially a single dune barrier enclosing a swamp or artificially drained flats.

The lowest land plant on the shore is sea rocket (*Cakile maritima*). This plant forms bright-green clumps of small fleshy leaves, pale mauve flowers and numerous seed-pods. It is common in this type of habitat worldwide, but thought to have been introduced to New Zealand by Europeans. Further up on the face of the foredune are the trailing silvery stems of spinifex (*Spinifex sericeus*) or the more robust clusters of bronze-green pingao (*Desmoschoenus spiralis*). Marram grass (*Ammophila arenaria*), introduced to stabilise sand dunes throughout New Zealand, is present on Great Barrier as a small patch on Medlands Beach and more extensively at the northern end of Kaitoke. A few metres further back are the bright pink trumpets of sand bindweed (*Calystegia soldanella*) and the cotton-wool heads of the introduced hare's-tail grass (*Lagurus ovatus*). Behind the first dune crest, shrubs may establish, in particular the sprawling pohuehue (*Muehlenbeckia complexa*), which forms a springy mat up to a metre deep. This protects the sand surface and enables introduced pasture grasses and other plants to establish.

In the past, native shrubs such as sand cassinia (*Cassinia leptophylla*), sand coprosma (*Coprosma acerosa*) and manuka would have formed a narrow border to native forest or kanuka scrub on the rear dunes, but most of this cover has been lost to pasture, buried by drifting sand or shaded out by pines planted to consolidate the sand. There were also many pohutukawa, their low-spreading branches often buried by sand. Remnants of this dune forest survive among the pines at northern Kaitoke. Dense tufts of astelia

(*Astelia banksii*) occur beneath the remaining pohutukawa and on their horizontal boughs, along with ground-covering and epiphytic ferns. Other trees include kanuka, mapou (*Mysine australis*), rangiora (*Brachyglottis repandra*) and hangehange (*Geniostoma rupestris*). Away from the shore, the trees and their understorey rapidly become more diverse, especially on the wetter flats. Pollen preserved in the rear-dune swamps suggests that matai (*Prumnopitys taxifolia*) forest clothed the dunes in pre-Maori times.

The characteristic plant of open sand flats is the sand sedge (*Carex pumila*). Its sparse leaf-tufts and spiky brown seedheads mark the course of its underground rhizome. The more stabilised flats at northern Kaitoke carry a community of the rushes, oioi (*Apodasmia similis*), *Baumea juncea* and *Isolepis nodosa*. Introduced grasses and hawkbit (*Leontodon taraxacoides*) invade as the flats dry out, and subsequently may be invaded by pampas grass (*Cortaderia selloana*), bush lupin (*Lupinus arboreus*) and manuka or flax (*Phormium tenax*).

Foredune at Kaitoke Beach. Note the spreading rhizome of pingao in the foreground, the dense tussock of introduced marram *(Ammophila arenaria)* behind and the silvery-green wisps of spinifex *(Spinifex sericeus)* between.

Len Doel

Behind this zone at northern Kaitoke lie shrub-covered dunes and flats. This cover mainly comprises manuka, hakea (predominantly *H. sericea* but also *H. gibbosa*) and occasional mingimingi (*Leucopogon fasciculatus*). The dunes are being invaded by wildling pines from parent trees planted to prevent dune erosion, but the flats are still predominantly covered by native plants. The ground cover is a damp mat of mosses, lichens and native herbs such as sundew (*Drosera auriculata*) and orchids (*Thelymitra* spp.).

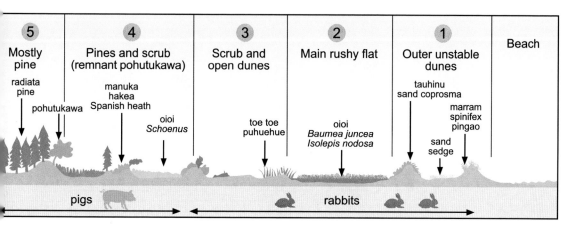

The low light intensity and the dense layer of undecomposed needles under the pines has reduced the ground cover to a few native ferns and monocotyledons. More species grow under the scattered pohutukawa trees, probably because here it is less shady and the leaf litter is very different; or these trees and their associated understory may be survivors of the original forest.

Transect across the Kaitoke dunes, showing mixed communities of native and exotic plants. Pines, hakea and erica are invading the system from the landward (left) side, while marram grass and introduced weeds invade the unstable dunes nearer the sea (far right). Introduced mammals disturb the natural processes and facilitate these invasions.

WETLANDS

Wetlands may be tidal (salt-marshes and mangrove forest), fresh water (floodplains, swamps), or areas of open water. These different habitats are often closely juxtaposed.

Saltwater wetlands have five main types of plant cover. The first is eelgrass (*Zostera novazelandica*), which forms dense mats on muddy shores that are only briefly exposed at low tide. The second type is the succulent glasswort

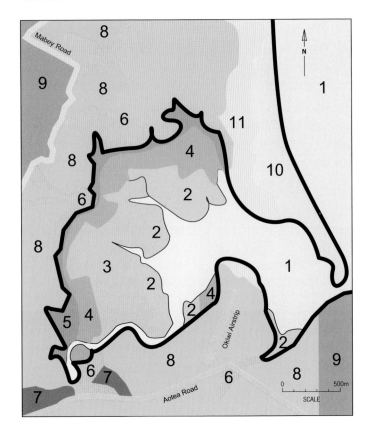

Vegetation map of Whangapoua harbour (modified after Cameron 1999) The zonation of vegetation types associated with degree of tidal influence can be clearly seen.
Key:
1, sea.
2, sparse mangroves.
3, denser mangroves.
4, sea rush.
5, *Baumea juncea*, sea rush, oioi and salt-meadow.
6, freshwater wetlands.
7, forest.
8, pasture.
9, regenerating scrub.
10, unconsolidated dunes.
11, stabilised dunes.

(*Sarcocornia quinquefolia*), which forms a thin turf higher on the shore. The third type is salt meadow, a mixture of species found on flats exposed to the air for longer. The main species are *Selliera radicans*, *Samolus repens*, *Triglochin striata* and saltwater paspalum (*Paspallum vaginatum*).

Mangroves or manawa (*Avicennia marina*), the fourth vegetation type, form a low forest in the intertidal zone,

Mangroves *(Avicennia marina)* at Whangapoua Harbour. Present research suggests that rapid siltation, caused by clearing the surrounding forest by fire and axe over the past 650 years, has transformed what was once a harbour into an estuary and led to the spread of mangroves.

Craig Potton

excluding most other land plants. A few mangroves occur along most estuary channels but more extensive areas line Whangapoua estuary and the heads of some of the western harbours.

The fifth type of saltwater wetland is found in the uppermost areas which are only briefly inundated by seawater during high tides. Here grow pure stands of oioi, sea rush (*Juncus kraussii*), *Baumea juncea* and the twiggy shrubs of swamp ribbonwood (*Plagianthus divaricatus*). This vegetation can be seen from the main road bridge over Kaitoke Creek, looking towards Hirakimata.

The zonation of these vegetation types can be clearly seen when looking over the Whangapoua estuary from Maybey Road. The outer zone of mangroves varies from scattered small shrubs to a continuous cover of two-metre-high trees further inland. Behind these are dense stands of sea rush, followed by oioi, *Baumea juncea* or salt meadow, and further back still are stands of manuka and freshwater swamp, large areas of which may be killed by surges of salt water during storms or exceptional spring tides, such as those which killed many hectares of manuka in Whangapoua and at Kaitoke Swamp in 1997.

Large freshwater swamps are (or were) found close to sea level behind the coastal dunes of the eastern bays. Draining some of these systems produced most of the fertile grazing land on the island; also undrained areas were sometimes grazed by cattle or burned. Nevertheless, the remaining freshwater swamps are still extensive and relatively unmodified wildlife habitats with high conservation value. They also are highly important for flood and sedimentation control.

The Kaitoke wetland is ranked as a site of special interest, with populations of endangered birds and a total of 163 plant species, of which about four-fifths are native, including several rare orchids. Parts of the swamp have been drained or burned and grazed. Pines (*Pinus radiata* and *P. pinaster*) are invading from the dunes, and the central sand ridges are infested with hakea (*Hakea gibbosa*). There are two impenetrable prickly shrubby species of *Hakea* which

Tangle fern *(Gleichenia dicarpa)* invading a stand of *Baumea juncea*, Kaitoke swamp.

Craig Potton

have invaded northern New Zealand from Australia: the other is *H. sericea*. Both have branches covered with woody seed pods which survive burning and open after fire to spread their seeds on to the ash-bed. The seedlings require high light and a mineral soil environment to establish, so consequently their spread is mainly determined by the frequency of fires.

The Whangaparara road traverses the southern arm of Kaitoke Swamp for about two kilometres, following a gradient of sediment and vegetation change. The central part of the swamp is made up of ancient sand dunes. The northern arm, into which Hot Springs Creek feeds, can be reached only on foot, and even then with difficulty. However, the inland parts of the swamp can be seen readily from the track to the hot springs. The swamp vegetation is composed mainly of rushes and similar plants up to three metres high, often forming patches. The vegetation pattern seems to vary depending on whether the swamp is being filled mainly with inorganic sediments from streams, or from organic matter accumulating as peat. Another factor is saltwater penetration at the eastern end of the swamp. Marine deposits under much of the present swamp indicate that this influence was much stronger in the past.

The sequence of terrestrialisation (the transition from marsh to dry land) at Kaitoke is most evident when travelling westward along the Whangaparapara road. It begins opposite the golf course, where the swamp vegetation comprises baumea (*Baumea juncea* and *B. rubiginosa*), tangle fern (*Gleichenia dicarpa*) and sparse patches of raupo (*Typha orientalis*). This mixture gradually merges into raupo and flax, which in turn are invaded by manuka and cabbage trees (*Cordyline australis*). Also present are pink bindweed (*Calystegia sepium*), swamp willow weed (*Polygonum salicifolium*), giant umbrella sedge (*Cyperus ustulatus*), *Bulboschoenus fluviatilis* and various other sedges, and swamp millet grass (*Isachne globosa*). Further up the arm beside the abutting hill slope is a narrow zone of kahikatea (*Dacrycarpus dacrydioides*) swamp forest, with kiekie (*Freycinetia banksii*) and huge cutty grass (*Gahnia xanthocarpa*). This community, which can be seen at the first boardwalk on the hot springs track, is being invaded by the alien weeds mistflower (*Ageratina riparia*), Mexican devil (*Ageratina adenophora*) and blackberry (*Rubus fruticosus*). Elsewhere, tiny remnants of a more mixed swamp forest occur. This features the rare swamp maire (*Syzygium maire*), with its upwardly looped breathing roots, and the towering pukatea (*Laurelia novaezelandiae*), with its spreading flange-like buttresses.

Freshwater swamps are among the most productive ecosystems known. At Kaitoke Swamp, for example, each year the raupo stands produce between two and three tonnes dry weight of organic matter per hectare — more than most tropical forests or intensively cultivated land. This organic matter is produced faster than it can break down, so the semi-decomposed leaves and stems are soon buried to a depth where they are permanently waterlogged, oxygen is cut off and decomposition stops completely. Peat then accumulates and a bog forms.

Although raupo is the most productive plant present, baumea and tangle fern are the main peat producers. Baumea flourishes where the water-table is close to the surface throughout the year and silt input is small. Most of its annual production of shoots and rhizomes accumulates undecomposed, so that peaty sediments rapidly build up. Tangle fern can then invade the baumea stands, contributing additional organic matter which further acidifies the substrate. The resulting raised swamp surface enables shrubs such as manuka to invade. However, raupo also can invade the tangle fern if re-flooding occurs, and extensive areas of this mixed community exist on the swamp.

Kaitoke Swamp has few areas of permanently open water, but one wetland where this does occur is the swamp in front of the police station at Claris. Here, *Baumea teretifolia* and *Eleocharis sphacelata* protrude from water that lies about half a metre deep over most of the area in summer. In the deeper water there are stands of raupo, *Eleocharis sphacelata* and *Baumea articulata*. A beautiful raupo swamp

Mexican devil *(Ageratina adenophora)*, an aggressive weed invading wetland on Kaitoke Swamp.

Tim Martin

with cabbage trees up to eight metres tall, flax and the straggling pink bindweed can be seen opposite the entrance to the Okiwi Recreational Reserve beside the Fitzroy–Claris road.

There used to be other places like Kaitoke Swamp in the freshwater wetlands of Great Barrier; for example, the Awana flats, on the east coast. These have now been mostly drained, leaving a sad remnant of grazed kahikatea and pukatea forest with a few nikau (*Rhopalostylis sapida*), puriri (*Vitex lucens*) and kanuka at the northern end (near Mickey's Campground), where the Awana Stream has contributed sand and silt. At the southern end, where sediment input from the surrounding slopes has been minimal, a few hectares of baumea and *Gleichenia* bog are hidden under a cover of manuka. Between the two, a few rotting stumps in the paddock tell of the former kahikatea forest, but nothing remains of the once extensive raupo and tangle-fern stands. With them have also gone the fernbirds, spotless crake and bittern. Where Awana Stream escapes to the sea, remnants of salt-marsh can be found along its banks and on the wetter parts of the alluvial flats. Here, a rapidly declining population of brown teal and one or two banded rail persist.

ALLUVIAL FLATS

Almost all Great Barrier's alluvial flats were once swamps, but have been burned and drained for agriculture and are now covered with a mixture of European grasses and exotic weeds, with patches of rushes. In some places — for example, landward of the main road between Claris and Medlands — they have reverted to dense manuka, with bracken (*Pteridium esculentum*) and water-fern (*Histiopteris incisa*) beneath. Their surface soils shrank with drainage and with added fertilisation from burning off the former manuka or fern cover, and are now organic silts with added wind-blown sand.

These flats are frequently inundated after heavy rain, and patches of wetland turf with estuarine species such as *Selliera radicans* and *Triglochin striata* occur; for example, close to the main drainage channels at the southern end of the Kaitoke flats. These wet flats currently support cattle and pukeko, along with smaller numbers of paradise shelducks and mallard. They are also utilised by brown teal and provide winter feeding grounds for oystercatchers (pied and variable) and pied stilts.

FOREST ECOSYSTEMS

The natural vegetation of most of Great Barrier is forest (land unit 10). The island can be divided into three main forest- and scrub-covered mountain blocks which differ in geology, climate and past land use, and show striking differences in vegetation. For example, kauri is abundant only in the central block (dominated by Mt Hobson at 621 metres, and Ahumata or White Cliffs), but even here fire and the axe have removed many trees. Scattered patches of kauri also occur in the northern block (dominated by Tataweka at 526 metres), but it is almost absent in the south (dominated by Ruahine at 402 metres).

Rocky outcrops to the north of the Windy Canyon–Hirakimata track, with kanuka *(Kunzea ericoides)* -dominated successional forest on the slopes. In the distance lie the alluvial paddocks of Okiwi airfield and the sandy flats and mangroves of Whangapoua estuary.

Len Doel

The upper part of Mt Hobson is composed of acidic volcanic rocks, and is subject to higher rainfall than the other peaks, so its soils are more leached of nutrients. The summit carries upper montane forest dominated by yellow-silver pine *(Lepidothamnus intermedius)* and other species restricted to this higher ground (eg. *Archeria racemosa*). Where the main components of this forest type are absent — for example, on Ruahine in the southern block — lowland broadleaf forest species grow to a higher altitude than they do on Mt Hobson. This situation suggests that, in the absence of the better-adapted high-altitude species, the lowland forest gains ascendancy, though it may be more due to differences between the soils formed by the rhyolitic rocks of Mt Hobson and the older weathered andesites of Ruahine. Similarly, there are differences between Mt Hobson and the northern block – with its underlying geology of Jurassic greywacke – though severe browsing by goats in this block may account for some of the differences. The abundance of raukawa *(Raukawa edgerleyi)* on Tataweka, and its virtual absence elsewhere, is hard to explain.

Great Barrier's forest cover varies with altitude, certain species dropping out and others appearing as altitude increases. Some species, such as kauri, cover the whole range and thus obscure this pattern. However, it is still possible to recognise four overlapping zones of mature forest:

- Coastal forest on cliffs and spurs within earshot of the sea but sometimes up to 160 metres above sea level.
- Lowland mixed broadleaf forest, to 250 metres a.s.l.
- Lower montane kauri-rimu-towai forest, mostly 200 to 340 metres a.s.l.
- Upper montane yellow-silver pine forest, commencing at around 340 metres but best developed on the summit of Mt Hobson at around 620 metres a.s.l.

Altitude is not the only variable affecting forest composition. For example, kahikatea-pukatea forest, with nikau and kiekie, was formerly common on waterlogged lowland alluvial flats, but this land has now been mostly cleared for farming. In the transition between lowland and montane forest, the composition of the forest depends more on topography than altitude. Ridges are often dominated by kauri or kanuka, mid-slopes by towai (*Weinmannia silvicola*), and gullies by pigeonwood (*Hedycarya arborea*), five-finger (*Pseudopanax arboreus*), tree ferns and supplejack (*Ripogonum scandens*).

History also plays a role. The reason pohutukawa (*Metrosideros excelsa*) is so abundant in the Hot Springs Creek valley could be because the area was a coastal gully six thousand years ago when most of the adjacent Kaitoke Swamp was tidal. As the sea retreated, the naturally high salt content of the springs could have meant pohutukawa and some other coastal species such as oioi were better adapted to hang on there. Disturbances such as logging and fire also have affected forest composition on Great Barrier.

COASTAL CLIFFS AND STEEP INFERTILE COASTAL SLOPES

Coastal cliffs, stacks and steep forested hillsides (land units 1 and 7) are found all around the coast of Great Barrier, but especially on the more rugged western side. The vegetation here is essentially forest, comprising a low-canopied

Coastal pohutukawa
(Metrosideros excelsa)
at Kiwiriki Bay.

Craig Potton

heathland (mainly manuka), or taller kanuka with a canopy moulded by the strong salt-laden winds, except on the rocky stacks, headlands and bluffs which are too harsh for even these hardy plants.

The characteristic coastal tree of Great Barrier is the pohutukawa. With its huge roots and branches spread-eagled across steep headlands, dark green foliage offsetting silvery new leaves, and abundant deep crimson flowers, this splendid tree is an icon of the island. Pohutukawa grow relatively quickly and can live for centuries, withstanding gales and salt spray and preventing rock faces from crumbling into the sea. On steep slopes and bluffs, the pohutukawa grow right down to sea level, and have a dense shrubby understorey of flax, kawakawa (*Macropiper excelsum*), rangiora (*Brachyglottis repanda*), karo (*Pittosporum crassifolium*) and hangehange (*Geniostoma rupestris*). Houpara (*Pseudopanax lessonii*) occurs in the damper gullies that run down to the sea. The perching lily (*Astelia banksii*) and epiphytic ferns (*Pyrrosia eleagnifolia* and *Microsorum pustulatum*) clothe the horizontal pohutukawa branches and the adjacent lichen-encrusted rocks.

Exposed headlands and stacks may bear shrubby hymenanthera (*Melicytus novae-zelandiae*) and the prostrate shiny green taupata (*Coprosma repens*). On the southern coast, near Cape Barrier, the pohutukawa community includes the small tree called wharangi (*Melicope ternata*), with its attractive bright green foliage and creamy flowers in spring. Elsewhere — for example, in the western harbours — spring is marked by the golden flowers of kowhai (*Sophora microphylla*), which attract kereru (wood pigeon).

The typical coastal forest of the island's northern block includes taraire (*Beilschmeidia tarairi*), pohutukawa, kohekohe (*Dysoxylum spectabile*) and tawa (*Beilschmeidia tawa*), along with less frequent stands of puriri (*Vitex lucens*), karaka (*Corynocarpus laevigatus*) and tawapou (*Pouteria costata*). As elsewhere, ponga (*Cyathea dealbata*), *Coprosma arborea, C. rhamnoides*, nikau and rangiora are common in the understorey and shrub layers.

Small pohutukawa cling to cliffs on the rugged, saltspray-swept western coast of Great Barrier.
DOC

Island plants, especially those close to the sea, typically have larger leaves than their mainland counterparts, as is seen with Great Barrier's splendid coastal nikau and stands of kawakawa, rangiora and broad-leafed tawa (*Beilschmeidia tawaroa*). The latter is characteristic of the coastal zone, and its upper limit of distribution, around 160 metres a.s.l., marks the top of the island's coastal forest zone.

Coastal forest rapidly gives way upwards into the lowland broadleaf forest, but in areas where this latter cover has now gone, degraded strips of coastal forest on cliff faces abruptly change into steep infertile coastal slopes, covered by coastal heathland with a wind-shorn canopy. On the most degraded soils this community is dominated by manuka a metre or two in height. Semi-prostrate forms of this shrub and of kanuka can also be found. Elsewhere, a surprising diversity of shrubs mix with the manuka, suggesting this community has been present for a long time. Coastal heathlands are currently being invaded by heather, especially the pink-flowered *Erica baccans*, and by hakea. Patches of flax are often a sign of prehistoric Maori habitations, which were concentrated on coastal headlands, dunes and river mouths. Forest was probably cleared from these coastal sites many centuries before Europeans came.

The coastal pohutukawa forests must formerly have been home to tuatara and many burrow-nesting seabirds. The birds must have been important providers of nitrogen and phosphorus, which are easily leached from steep situations. Apparently only one tiny colony of grey-faced petrel now remains, although the inaccessible nature of these habitats and the nocturnal activities of petrels and shearwaters mean that other species may be as yet undetected. Blue penguins are fairly common.

LOWLAND MIXED BROADLEAF FOREST

Broadleaf forest probably used to cover most aspects and slopes up to at least 250 metres everywhere on Great Barrier. On the shady south-facing slope of the Kaiarara Valley towards Mt Hobson, lowland broadleaf forest begins at around 60 to 80 metres a.s.l. Across the valley on the north-

facing slope a more open forest occurs, often with a few tall kanuka or rewarewa (*Knightia excelsa*), indicating past disturbance.

The canopy of the south-facing forest comprises mainly taraire and puriri, but tawa, tawaroa, maire (*Nestegis lanceolata*) and kohekohe are also present. The abundance of kohekohe seedlings and saplings, with their large pinnate leaves, is a striking feature of this forest type on Great Barrier. Elsewhere in New Zealand possums are ravaging this species, and regeneration is rare.

Puriri trees, especially those on ridges near the upper limit of their distribution, can be up to two metres in diameter and carry whole communities of epiphytic plants on their huge horizontal branches. These communities include large clumps of perching lilies (*Collospermum hastatum* and *Astelia* spp.), orchids (*Earina* spp. and *Winikia cunninghamii*), climbing rata (*Metrosideros perforata*), ferns

Lowland mixed broadleaf forest at Kiwiriki Bay. Rangiora (*Brachyglottis repandra*) and *Collospermum hastatum* grow on a fallen tree (right foreground); tutu (*Coriaria arborea*) at left and whau (*Entelea arborescens*) in the centre. In the middle distance are the tree ferns wheki (*Dicksonia squarrosa*) (left) and mamaku (*Cyathea medullaris*), and two nikau palms (*Rhopalostylis sapida*) at far left. The canopy behind is mainly pohutukawa (*Metrosideros excelsa*).

Craig Potton

A fine stand of regenerating nikau palms beneath pohutukawa and puriri *(Vitex lucens)* at Kiwiriki Bay. Most of the nikau palms here are young, but mature specimens on Great Barrier have larger leaves than their mainland counterparts – up to five metres long.

Craig Potton

such as *Pyrrhosia elaeagnifolius* and *Phymatosorus diversifolius*, filmy ferns, mosses and lichens. The tall canopy species cast a dense shade, and the forest floor is a rubble of loose stones and leaf-litter, with a scattering of ground ferns. Occasional large specimens of northern rata (*Metrosideros robusta*) emerge above the forest canopy.

Where the dense, shade-casting tarairi is less common, the forest often has an understorey of tall shrubs, tree ferns, nikau palms and sub-canopy trees. As already noted, several of these lowland forest species appear to grow higher up on Ruahine than on Mt Hobson. For example, puriri and kohekohe both disappear before 250 metres in the Kaiarara Valley, but can be found close to the summit of Ruahine at around 400 metres. The same applies to half a dozen other species, including mahoe (*Melicytus ramiflorus*) and kiekie.

The transition from lowland to montane forest occurs quite rapidly in the Kaiarara Valley, at about the level of the first kauri dam. Kohekohe, puriri and taraire largely disappear, and towai or tawa dominate the canopy, with Hall's totara (*Podocarpus hallii*), rimu, kauri and hinau (*Elaeocarpus dentatus*) all becoming more conspicuous. The first true upper montane species also occur, with tawairi

(*Ixerba brexioides*), toatoa (*Phyllocladus toatoa*) and Kirk's pine (*Halocarpus kirkii*) appearing for the first time. On Mt Hobson, these species appear to out-compete the lowland broadleaf trees, which are thus restricted to lower altitudes. Tawairi is a characteristic tree of the wet mountain summits and leached soils in the Auckland region.

Before the arrival of kiore (*Rattus exulans*) and extensive clearance by fire and axe, the birdlife of Great Barrier's lowland broadleaf forests must have been prolific (see Chapter 9). Today, the lowland forest's seasonal flowers and fruit constitute the main food resource for kereru (wood pigeon) and tui, although these birds also visit higher places.

LOWER MONTANE FOREST

Above the Kaiarara dam, the forest is a mosaic of kanuka on dry north-facing ridges, and elsewhere a mixture of canopy trees that include towai, hinau, rewarewa and toro (*Myrsine salicina*). Emergent rimu and miro (*Prumnopitys ferruginea*) occur, as do some large kauri and smaller 'ricker' kauri trees. Although kauri occur from sea level to the summit of Mt Hobson, it was in this zone that the large straight trees were most numerous, so the forest was much disturbed by logging last century. Some idea of the former grandeur of these forests is evident from the magnificent 'stringers' used in the

Interior of the upper montane forest on Mt Hobson. In the foreground are *Alseuosmia* and *Quintinia serrata*. The twisted trunks, clothed with kidney fern (*Trichomanes reniforme*) and mosses, are mainly yellow - silver pine (*Lepidothamnus intermedius*).

Tim Martin

construction of the lower dam, and large stumps now well hidden by ferns and bushes in the vicinity.

Kauri usually regenerates after large-scale forest destruction. The first coloniser is tea-tree (manuka and kanuka), then kauri seedlings become established in the moderate shade cast by this scrub as it ages. As a consequence, kauri forests often exhibit one or two 'cohorts'; that is, groups of trees all of similar age. The older cohort may represent the first regeneration phase, while the younger trees often are individuals that have colonised gaps created later by fallen trees, especially on rocky knolls and steep ridges.

Charcoal preserved in the swamps clearly indicates that large areas of Great Barrier's forest were burned by Maori about 650 years ago, probably to encourage bracken fern (*Pteridium esculentum*), the root of which was a staple food (aruhe). The first cohort of kauri regeneration therefore would have been a dense stand about 550 years old, with trunks a metre or more in diameter, when the Europeans logged it. Europeans, too, burned large areas of forest, to

View back towards Windy Canyon and the upper Awana catchment from high on the slopes of Mt Hobson. Young regenerating kauri *(Agathis australis)* in foreground. This whole area was burned in the 1920s, with a few standing dead trees indicating the former forest structure. The present canopy is mainly manuka *(Leptospermum scoparium)* and towai *(Weinmannia silvicola)*. The rare endemics *Kunzea sinclairii* and *Olearia allomii* occur beside the track following the watershed (left).

Len Doel

clear the land for mining, gum-digging and farming. Many areas of Great Barrier consequently have suffered two separate cycles of burning and soil erosion. With the topsoil and seed sources largely removed, it is no wonder that these areas are slow to regenerate, and are now classified as land unit 9, 'low fertility hills'.

The montane forests of Mt Hobson are also characterised by the increasing prevalence of toatoa, rimu and tawairi at greater altitudes. Commonly associated with tawairi are understorey trees such as tawheowheo (*Quintinia serrata*), the attractive shrub *Pseudopanax discolor*, and graceful clumps of cutty grass (*Gahnia setifolia*).

UPPER MONTANE FOREST

The air in the montane forest of Mt Hobson is cool and damp. Filmy ferns and mosses clothe fallen logs and twisted trunks. Yellow-silver pine is the dominant tree, but kauri, Kirk's pine, toatoa, tawairi and hinau are also common. Southern rata (*Metrosideros umbellata*) is present near the summit. The understorey contains tawheowheo, the purple-flowered *Hebe macrophylla*, *Coprosma dodonaefolia*, *Dracophyllum patens*, *Pittosporum kirkii*, *Corokia buddlioides*, *Epacris pauciflora* and *Archeria racemosa*. This forest type is restricted to the summit of Mt Hobson, above 550 metres, although most of its characteristic species are also present in the lower kauri-rimu-towai zone, becoming progressively more common above the upper kauri dam (around 340 metres a.s.l.).

A view across the rocky rhyolitic outcrops at Windy Canyon, down the Awana Valley to the distant flats and Awana Bay. The grey spreading patch on the upper part of the outcrop at far right is *Kunzea sinclairii*. In the foreground is a young kauri tree. The manuka-covered hills (behind the rocks, centre right) were logged for kauri and burned early last century.

Len Doel

Mixed conifer forest similar to that on Mt Hobson may have covered much of Northland 40,000 years ago, before the last glacial period. The summits of several mountains in the Hauraki Gulf area contain relics of this ancient forest — Moehau, on Coromandel Peninsula; Hauturu (Little Barrier); and Table Mountain in the Kauaeranga Valley, south of Thames . The trees of this ancient forest are slow-growing and long-lived. Cores taken from the trunks of quite small kauri trees near the summit of Mt Hobson show them to be more than 600 years old.

The montane forest is quiet apart from the occasional trill of a grey warbler or the harsh cry of a kaka. At night, moreporks are common, and as the higher forest is reached the harsh rattle of black petrels can sometimes be heard. Several hundred of these birds nest in burrows under logs and among the damp rocks of the summit zone.

TEA-TREE SCRUB AND SUCCESSIONAL FOREST

Because much of the original forest has been cleared by logging and fire, the most widespread vegetation type on Great Barrier Island is now regenerating kanuka and manuka. These 'pioneer' species are collectively known as tea-tree scrub (land unit 8). Good examples can be seen on the hot springs track and just beyond the south fork on the Kaiarara dam track. Here the kanuka canopy is 12 to 15 metres high, overtopping silver tree fern (*Cyathea dealbata*), nikau and a few shrubs. A line of large black mamaku (*C. medullaris*) marks the former tramway along which logs were hauled to the coast. At that time, the surrounding slopes would have been a charred wilderness of stumps and shattered trees.

Succession on a clear-felled area usually starts with manuka and kanuka. Because kanuka is more shade-tolerant, taller and longer-lived than manuka, it gradually becomes predominant. As the manuka dies out, after 15 to 20 years, the lower canopy opens up to provide more light and space for established seedlings of shrubs such as five-finger, pigeonwood and rangiora. The kanuka canopy may persist for a century or more while the community it

nurtures grows in stature and diversity. This successional process is one of the main ways that kauri forests become established.

Tea-tree communities at different stages of regenerating to more complex forests cover a larger area than any other ecosystem on Great Barrier Island, and are intrinsically valuable as a reservoir of natural biodiversity. They represent the healing of the landscape after centuries of exploitation and are a key element in both creating the island's distinctive scenic character and restoring the complex of mature forest gradients.

Rosalie Bay with distant Cuvier Island (left) and the Mercury Islands. In the foreground are a cabbage tree and a canopy of kanuka. A more varied canopy of lowland broadleaf species and nikau palms occurs on the slopes to the left.

Len Doel

HEATHLANDS

Low scrubby tea-tree communities on steep slopes above the coastal cliffs (land unit 7) often grade into taller tea-tree further inland. These coastal heaths have already been described (p.68). Low-fertility hills mostly represent places where the loss of topsoil following repeated fires has been so extensive that plant growth and reversion to forest is now very slow, as can be seen when ascending Te Ahumata or approaching Mt Hobson from the Windy Canyon side.

On Te Ahumata, heathlands may date from long before the arrival of Europeans, but the presence of kauri gum in the soil indicates that a kauri forest once stood there. The predominant shrub on the summit is dense manuka, a metre or less in height, although occasional pohutukawa occur well above their normal range on the cliffs, reflecting their ability to grow in exposed areas as long as they receive plenty of light.

On the Windy Canyon track the heathland contains two species unique to Great Barrier Island: Great Barrier tea-tree (*Kunzea sinclairii*) and the daisy shrub *Olearia allomii*. The former, with its silky grey leaves, is a creeping or semi-prostrate relation of kanuka, while the daisy shrub has showy white flowers and rounded dark green leathery leaves two to four centimetres long.

Great Barrier's high heathlands occupy acidic soils degraded by repeated fires, soil erosion and leaching. They may take centuries to revert to the kauri-rimu-towai forest that presumably once grew there. When this process is complete, the rocky outcrops, such as those on the Windy Canyon track, will remain as 'islands' on which the endemic heathland species survive.

Grazed alluvial flats and a patch of *Eucalyptus* trees (centre). The road traverses drained swampland, and beyond it are holiday homes on the more consolidated rear dune.

Len Doel

GRAZED ECOSYSTEMS

Great Barrier's alluvial flats, cleared foothills and lower slopes (land unit 5), along with steeper slopes close to the sea (land unit 6), are now predominantly used for grazing cattle. In some cases these have carried fern, scrub or grassland for centuries, indicating on-going clearance by humans. The area of pasture on Great Barrier is diminishing with the decline of farming caused by low productivity, summer droughts and increasing costs. The vegetation cover is surprisingly diverse, but is mostly exotic grasses, including *Agrostis* spp., *Anthoxanthum odoratum* and *Holcus lanatus,* and many exotic wildflower species. The ubiquitous manuka and exotic woody weeds such as heather soon invade once the pasture is 'let go', sprouting up in small areas laid bare by overgrazing and erosion.

The pastures are the main habitat for a number of birds. Wetter areas have pukeko and paradise shelducks, while the open slopes have native pipits and have recently been invaded by spur-winged plover. In the winter, small flocks of starlings and mynahs feed on pasture grubs, while goldfinches, greenfinches and sparrows feed predominantly on weed seeds.

RESTORING LOST ECOSYSTEMS

Unlike some of the smaller islands of the Hauraki Gulf, such as Tiri Tiri Matangi, there is no need to replant the forest on Great Barrier. The tea-tree 'nurseries' that cover so much of the island are doing this job through succession. This process may take centuries in areas where topsoil has been removed, and which are furthest from surviving forest remnants, but it is proceeding fast in the wetter gullies and close to seed sources, as can be seen on the old kauri logging road to the hot springs. The coastal heathlands also are slowly reverting to forest.

Three major threats could reverse or delay this process: fire, woody weeds and introduced mammals. The risk posed by each will increase as the human population grows and land subdivision continues. Only if that population values the natural ecosystems will the ecological restraints outlined in the Auckland City Council's district plan stand a chance of being effective.

The most immediate concern is fire prevention, as tea-tree stands are extremely flammable. Fire would destroy the young forests they nurture and lead to the explosive spread of the more fire-resistant woody weeds, especially hakea, wattles and pines. Hakea are already abundant in the manuka covering the eastern hills. Fire would also cause further spread of heather and gorse. All these species thrive on soils eroded after fire, and build-up of their highly flammable dead twigs and leaves risks further fires.

If fire can be prevented, especially over the next few decades, it will be possible to break the cycle of fire, loss of soil nutrients and colonisation by fire-promoting woody weeds that threatens restoration on Great Barrier. Hakea and most other woody weeds live only a few decades, and without a fire to stimulate germination they will be progressively eliminated from the developing forest. The same probably applies to *Pinus radiata*, although the process will take longer. The native forest that replaces the scrub will be much less susceptible to fire.

Keeping mammals out is another important step in the restoration of Great Barrier's dune, wetland and forest ecosystems. The coastal pohutukawa and lowland broadleaf forests would be seriously at risk if possums were to get loose. Goats have ravaged the northern block, and there are fallow deer on Kaikoura Island. Keeping Great Barrier free of stoats, weasels and ferrets is essential for the survival of birds like brown teal. Stray dogs and wild cats also are a threat. Rats and pigs are present throughout, even in the centre of Kaitoke Swamp. Rabbits seriously threaten the dune ecosystems, and could frustrate attempts to establish lowland forest in areas adjacent to pasture.

The central forest block contains some of the best remaining forest on the island. Full restoration of this forest should have high priority. If predators were eliminated, these forests could once more ring to noisy flocks of parakeets, chattering whiteheads and the call of bellbirds. Tracks to the black petrel nesting sites are a great boon to visitors, but they also make easy access for feral cats. Conservation of the montane forest ecosystem will involve managing not only the forest and its native lifeforms, but also the alien species that visit.

It is the coastal zone which is most under threat from future development. The northern end of the Kaitoke dunes has the largest area of dune vegetation remaining on Great Barrier, but this could be almost eliminated by future airport or industrial development. Swamps such as Kaitoke and the Whangapoua estuary are among the largest remaining wetland ecosystems in the Auckland region and contain small surviving populations of endangered bird species. Their hydrology, and hence their vegetation cover, is controlled largely by the vegetation cover of the catchments that feed them. They, in turn, affect the hydrology and stability of the dunes.

On Great Barrier, conservation should focus not so much on preserving remnant examples of past landscapes and their associated flora and fauna, but on the integration of adjacent ecosystems and on sustainable land use. Control of fire, weeds and introduced mammals is essential to the success of such a programme. The aspirations of the island's residents, visitors and managers largely coincide in a desire for the long-term use, enjoyment and conservation of Great Barrier's diverse ecosystems. Fulfilment of these ideals will depend on a commitment to setting goals and managing the linkages between these systems.

CHAPTER FIVE

FLORA

The low-growing Great Barrier kanuka (*Kunzea sinclairii*) is one of only two plants endemic to Great Barrier. It flowers prolifically in spring.

Ewen Cameron

Great Barrier supports more than 560 native vascular plant species: nearly a quarter of New Zealand's total flora. This is 45 percent more species than found on the Chatham Islands, and only four percent less than the number found on Stewart Island.

Great Barrier's special botanical features include endemic species (Great Barrier kanuka, *Kunzea sinclairii; Olearia allomii* and possibly an undescribed *Hebe*) and 75 nationally or regionally threatened and uncommon plants, which include at least 17 presumed locally extinct species. Fifteen species on the island are at their New Zealand northernmost geographical limit, and one is at its southern limit. Thirteen species have only been seen on the smaller islands around Great Barrier. Many plants are confined to

the 40 hectares of forest around the summit of Mt Hobson (Hirakimata) that were never logged or burnt.

Apart from the lichens, Great Barrier's non-vascular plants (mosses, liverworts, lichens, seaweeds) and fungi have been poorly studied. Two hundred and forty-seven species of lichens have been recorded on Great Barrier, almost a quarter of New Zealand's lichens. One study of mosses in the Miners Cove catchment recorded 84 species. As with the vascular plants, some of Great Barrier's lichens and mosses have a northern North Island distribution, and several other lichens reach their New Zealand northern limit on the island. Sixty-six seaweeds have been recorded from north-eastern Great Barrier.

The largest island associated with Great Barrier, Kaikoura (564 hectares) has been studied only briefly, but Rakitu (Arid) Island (350 hectares) on the eastern side has a recorded flora of 240 native vascular species and 124 lichens.

Great Barrier has been connected to the mainland for most of the last 18 million years, and therefore lacks the high number of endemic species found on islands that have been isolated for much longer, such as the Three Kings, or that never were connected to the mainland, like the Kermadec Islands. Most of the species on Great Barrier also occur on the Coromandel Peninsula, and the elevated central forest area of Great Barrier has strong similarities with upland areas of the Coromandel Ranges and Little Barrier Island (see panel, p.85)

The first botanist to study the flora of Great Barrier was Thomas Kirk, an Englishman who spent nearly two months there in 1867–68. His early description of the flora, and the specimens he collected, are valuable because since then so much vegetation has been destroyed and many species have become extinct. Fanny Osborne (1852–1933), an artist who lived at Tryphena, painted exquisite watercolours of native plants. Other botanists include staff of the University of Auckland and the Auckland Museum, which now has more than 4,500 pressed plant specimens from Great Barrier.

The extinct Adam's mistletoe (*Trilepidea adamsii*) was painted early in the twentieth century on Great Barrier by Fanny Osborne. She was one of few artists to record its true colour.

(Watercolour, Auckland War Memorial Museum).

GREAT BARRIER FLORA — LIMITS AND STATUS

The following lists Great Barrier plants at their New Zealand geographical limits, their status on the island and whether they also are present on Little Barrier Island.

Key
* = also occurs on Little Barrier
PE = presumed extinct on Great Barrier
E = endemic to Great Barrier
S = southern New Zealand geographical limit
N = northern New Zealand geographical limit

Ferns
Grammitis patagonica N

Trees and shrubs
Clianthus maximus ? N, PE
Dracophyllum patens N
Hebe macrocarpa var. *latisepala** N
Hebe pubescens* N
Hebe 'Great Barrier' E
Kunzea sinclairii E
Metrosideros parkinsonii* N
Olearia allomii E
Pomaderris hamiltonii N
Pseudopanax discolor* N
Pseudopanax simplex N

Herbs
Arthropodium candidum N
Colensoa physaloides S
Leptinella dioica ssp. *dioica* N
Leptinella squalida ssp. *squalida* N, PE
Polygonum plebeium N, PE
Thelymitra formosa N
Vittadina australis N, PE

COMPARISON OF FLORA ON THREE
HAURAKI GULF MOUNTAIN PEAKS

In 1973 botanist Lucy Moore compared the summit flora of Mt Hobson on Great Barrier (627 m), Mt Moehau on Coromandel (892) and Little Barrier (722). A feature of note is that 22 montane vascular plants do not reach the Barrier Islands, but find their northernmost limit on Mt Moehau, which is higher and further south. Many species occur on all three peaks, but some are unexpectedly absent from one, two or all three summits, which suggests that dispersal is an important limiting factor.

• Plants on Great Barrier's summit but not recorded from either Little Barrier or Mt Moehau:
Dracophyllum patens, Epacris pauciflora var. *sinclairii, Halocarpus kirkii, Kunzea sinclairii, Monoao colensoi, Olearia allomii.*

• Plants on Great and Little Barrier summits but not recorded on Mt Moehau:
Archeria racemosa, Metrosideros parkinsonii, Pseudopanax discolor.

• Plants on Little Barrier and Mt Moehau summits but not recorded on Great Barrier's summit:
Dracophyllum traversii, Griselinia littoralis, Peraxilla tetrapetala, Collospermum microspermum.
(While *C. microspermum* has not been recorded from the central summit area, it has been from the northern high point of Great Barrier, at Tataweka.)

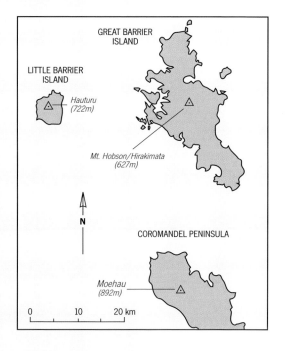

FERNS AND FERN ALLIES (119 SPECIES)

Ferns are common in all New Zealand forests, but Great Barrier is particularly rich in them, having more than half of all New Zealand species. There are six species of tree fern. The tallest, black tree fern or mamaku (*Cyathea medullaris*), is frequent in the wetter areas, but the most unusual is *Dicksonia lanata*, strangely unknown from Little Barrier and scarce on the Coromandel Ranges. This short tree fern of the central heathlands develops a trunk only one metre tall. Its stiff, harsh fronds, which are long-stalked, distinguish it from other tree ferns. Soft tree fern (*Cyathea smithii*), characterised by a skirt of hanging midribs, is only known in the north by Tataweka, and is oddly absent from the Mt Hobson/Hirakimata area.

Soft tree fern at Tataweka.
Ewen Cameron

Blechnum norfolkianum on Rakitu Island.
Ewen Cameron

Loxsoma cunninghamii, an endemic fern of northern New Zealand.
Ewen Cameron

Lycopodiella cernua, one of the six club mosses growing on Great Barrier. Most occur on the open track margins from the canyon to Mt Hobson.
Ewen Cameron

Two distinctive ferns of warm northern New Zealand islands are *Blechnum norfolkianum* and *Pteris comans*. The former occurs only on offshore islands as far south as Mayor Island. In the Great Barrier group, it is only known on Rakitu Island, where it is locally common in forest. The larger *Pteris comans* is found in most coastal forest areas within the Great Barrier group, and south to the Bay of Plenty. The more southern of the two thermal hot pools in the Kaitoke wetland is bordered with a lush growth of pure umbrella fern, *Sticherus flabellatus*.

In the Kaitoke hot pools and adjoining streams is often the prolific growth, especially in the summer, of a cyanobacteria (or blue-green alga), *Schizothrix calcicola*. This species has unbranched filaments that intertwine and form extensive mats where the water temperature is 34–42°C.

A fern ally and two ferns are possibly now extinct on Great Barrier: *Phylloglossum drummondii*, king fern (*Marattia salicina*) and *Lindsaea viridis*. Some ferns are very limited in distribution; for example, a tufted filmy fern (*Trichomanes strictum*) and a number of tiny *Grammitis* species with small, strap-like fronds occur only in the central upland moss-forest. *Loxsoma cunninghamii*, with fronds greenish yellow above and whitish below, is common on clay banks in central Great Barrier. Its general distribution is from Kaitaia to the Coromandel Ranges. Narrow comb ferns (*Schizaea bifida* and *S. dichotoma*) can also be found on the central clay banks. Two tiny adder-tongue ferns (*Ophioglossum* spp.) occur by the streams in the Te Paparahi area.

CONIFERS (13 SPECIES)

Kauri (*Agathis australis*) is the largest conifer on Great Barrier. Impressive surviving remnants of kauri forest occur especially around Mt Hobson, the Harataonga Scenic Reserve and locally in eastern Te Paparahi. Some of these trees are more than 2.3 metres in diameter. Kauri regeneration is locally prolific in central Great Barrier. Eight kauri rickers were found for the first time on Rakitu Island in 1980, the seed having blown across from Great Barrier.

One of the isolated stands of mature kauri forest in eastern Te Paparahi.

Ewen Cameron

Conifers are most common and diverse in the central area of Great Barrier. Yellow-silver pine (*Lepidothamnus intermedius*) is common in the Mt Hobson/Hirakimata area of Great Barrier. It also occurs on the Coromandel Ranges southwards, but is absent elsewhere in the Auckland region and is known further north only at Waipoua Forest. Toatoa (*Phyllocladus toatoa*), with its large celery-like 'leaves', and Kirk's pine (*Halocarpus kirkii*) can be seen around Mt Hobson and Maungapiko. Silver pine (*Monoao colensoi*) is highly localised, by Mt Hobson. Kawaka (*Libocedrus plumosa*), rimu (*Dacrydium cupressinum*), kahikatea (*Dacrycarpus dacrydioides*), totara (*Podocarpus totara*), Hall's totara (*P. hallii*), matai (*Prumnopitys taxifolia*) and miro (*P. ferruginea*) are more widespread on Great Barrier, but rarely common.

Kirk's pine at Maungapiko.

Ewen Cameron

TREES AND SHRUBS (130 SPECIES)

Puriri (*Vitex lucens*) on Great Barrier often have massive trunks two to three metres in diameter. They occur throughout the island, even on ridge-tops, and occasionally compete for growing space with another significant tree, the northern rata (*Metrosideros robusta*). Northern rata start life perching in the branches of a host tree, putting roots down to the ground, and finally over-topping and shading their hosts. But puriri are hard to kill, and places can be seen where both trees have fallen over during their struggle, only to grow erect again to continue their fight for light. Kanuka (*Kunzea ericoides*) is Great Barrier's most common tree and is present throughout, sometimes in pure stands. With trunks up to one metre in diameter, they may be New Zealand's largest specimens.

The myrtle family is well represented on Great Barrier by 15 species of tree, shrub and vine. The most impressive of these is pohutukawa (*Metrosideros excelsa*), which also form hybrids with northern tree rata. Southern rata (*M. umbellata*) occurs by Mt Hobson as narrow small trees.

Pohutukawa flowering on Rakitu around Christmas time.

Ewen Cameron

Because of its unique distribution, Parkinson's rata is the most remarkable of the nine species of *Metrosideros* (including five vines) present on Great Barrier.

Ewen Cameron

Dracophyllum patens at Mt Hobson.

Ewen Cameron

Tawari with early summer flowers.

Ewen Cameron

A scrambling shrub with scarlet flowers, Parkinson's rata (*M. parkinsonii*) has a remarkable distribution, being known only from the summit areas of Great and Little Barrier Islands and the South Island's west coast. No other plant shares this patchy distribution. It was named after Sydney Parkinson, the botanical artist on Cook's first voyage to New Zealand.

Dracophyllum patens, a narrow, shrubby member of the southern heath family, grows up to two metres tall and reaches its northern occurrence on Mt Hobson. It is also known on Great Barrier from Ahumata and the canyon area, and otherwise only from a few areas in the Coromandel Ranges. The taller epacrid shrub, *Archeria racemosa*, has leaves with parallel veins, a characteristic of this southern heath family. It reaches its northern geographical limit on Mt Hobson and on Little Barrier. Bunches of hanging bell-shaped flowers appear in the summer.

Another epacrid shrub, *Epacris pauciflora* var. *sinclairii*, is limited to higher areas on Great Barrier and the Coromandel Ranges. It can be distinguished from the more widely distributed var. *pauciflora* by its bushier habit, less pointed leaves and less obvious flowers. Hutu (*Ascarina lucida*) has toothed leaves and on Great Barrier is known only from this central area. It is found only in a few parts of northern New Zealand. Another plant of the central high area is tawari (*Ixerba brexioides*), a round-headed tree with leathery, coarsely toothed leaves. Flower buds form in

autumn, but the large white waxy flowers do not open until summer. It often grows with the wavy-leafed quintinia (*Quintinia serrata*).

Great Barrier's two endemic species are confined to the central heathlands. Great Barrier kanuka is a prostrate shrub with leaves so hairy that they appear silvery. It also grows in erect forms which may be hybrids with kanuka, and it may even hybridise with manuka. Initially, forest clearance would have benefited this sun-demanding species, but present regeneration is now shading it out of much of its present range, restricting it to cliffs, slips, tracks and stream margins.

The other endemic species, *Olearia allomii*, grows to two metres high and frequently occurs with Great Barrier kanuka. Its thicker leaves and earlier flowering (late spring) separate it from the rather similar akepiro (*O. furfuracea*).

The shrubby five-finger, *Pseudopanax discolor*, with its distinctive reddish bronze leaves, occurs in the central heathlands and also on the Coromandel Ranges and Little Barrier, but is absent elsewhere in the Auckland region. Three generally uncommon pittosporums (*Pittosporum huttonianum, P. kirkii* and *P. virgatum*) also occur in this central area.

A five-finger, *Pseudopanax discolor,* near Mt Hobson with young fruit.
Ewen Cameron

The second of Great Barrier's two endemic plants, *Olearia alomii.*
Ewen Cameron

Koromiko, *Hebe pubescens*, reaches its northern limit on the islands off the northern tip of Te Paparahi.

Ewen Cameron

Five types of koromiko (*Hebe* spp.) are present on Great Barrier. *H. stricta* is widespread throughout northern New Zealand. *H. macrocarpa* var. *latisepala* is endemic to Coromandel and the Barrier islands. *H. pubescens* has a similar distribution but is also recorded west of Auckland. *H. parviflora* occurs from Whangarei Heads to the top of the South Island, and possibly an undescribed endemic koromiko is present.

Pomaderris hamiltonii, a shrub up to three metres tall, was first recognised on the island in 1992 and often grows with its close relatives, kumerahau (*P. kumeraho*) and tauhinu (*P. phylicifolia*). Two horopito species (*Pseudowintera axillaris* and *P. colorata*) are present. The former is most common on the higher central slopes of the island. *P. colorata* has been seen only once, in 1980, when

A showy koromiko, *Hebe macrocarpa* var. *latisepala*.

Ewen Cameron

three shrubs were found in windswept scrub by Windy Hill. It is scarce north of the Coromandel Ranges and is distinguished from the closely related *P. axillaris* by its yellowish, red-splotched hot-tasting leaves. Raukawa (*Raukaua edgerleyi*), with its lemon-scented leaves, appears to be confined to the Tataweka area.

'Warmth-loving' offshore island species include coastal maire (*Nestegis apetala*), of the olive family. It occurs on northern Te Paparahi, the islands off the northern tip, and Rakitu. The outer island form of kawakawa (*Macropiper excelsum* subsp. *peltatum*) occurs on a single islet off the southern end of the main island. The normal form (subsp. *excelsum*) is frequent throughout. Coastal mahoe (*Melicytus novae-zelandiae*) is virtually confined to the outer islands of the group.

Great Barrier possibly used to be the northern limit for kaka beak (*Clianthus maximus*), with its large hanging scarlet flowers. This was collected by Kirk and painted on the island early in the twentieth century by Fanny Osborne. However, it has not been recorded since and now exists in the wild only on the East Cape region of the North Island, although it is grown in many New Zealand gardens. Likewise, sand pimelea (*Pimelea arenaria*) recorded by Kirk and last seen in 1919 on Great Barrier, is now extinct throughout the Auckland region.

CLIMBERS (22 SPECIES)

The large white rata (*Metrosideros albiflora*) is one of five forest rata vines present on Great Barrier. This one occurs in the central summit area and has the largest flowers and leaves of any rata. It grows in upland areas of Northland and as far south as East Cape. Coastal morning glory (*Ipomoea cairica*), with its large mauve flowers, is only known from Mahuki (Anvil) Island, where the gannets nest, and at the Claris landfill site. Tiritiri Matangi Island is probably the natural southern limit of this species, which extends north to the tropics. Mawhai (*Sicyos australis*), of the cucumber family, a coastal climber with spiny, dry fruit, now appears to be restricted to Rakitu.

Mawhai on Rakitu. Cucumber mosaic virus is suspected to have caused this plant to become nationally threatened. Male flowers stalked, female sessile.

Ewen Cameron

MISTLETOE (3 SPECIES)

Adam's mistletoe (*Trilepidea adamsii*) is one of only five New Zealand endemic plants now thought to be totally extinct. A bushy, partly parasitic shrub up to one metre across, it was New Zealand's most colourful mistletoe (see p. 83). It once occurred from Waipoua Forest to the Waikato, including Great Barrier and Waiheke Islands, and was last seen in 1954 in the Waikato.

The two mistletoes still present are the tiny *Korthalsella salicornioides*, usually parasitic on manuka and kanuka, and the larger green-flowered mistletoe (*Ileostylus micranthus*), which was first discovered in the late 1900s on kanuka in southern Great Barrier.

DICOTYLEDON HERBS (108 SPECIES)

Great Barrier is a stronghold of the creeping fuchsia (*Fuchsia procumbens*), with its erect flowers. This northern North Island coastal species reaches its southern limit on the Coromandel Peninsula. The island is also a regional stronghold of *Scleranthus biflorus*, which forms low hummocks on coastal rocks. It once grew on Auckland's volcanic cones. Cook's scurvy grass (*Lepidium oleraceum*), a spreading herb up to half a metre tall, is only known on Great Barrier from the Broken Islands, with its main population by the gannet colony on Mahuki Island. Today, it is virtually restricted to New Zealand's offshore islands.

Creeping fuchsia by a stream mouth, Te Paparahi.

Ewen Cameron

A forget-me-not, *Myosotis spathulata*, is only known from a single coastal collection from Te Paparahi in 1983. *Colensoa physaloides*, another 'warmth-loving' plant, grows up to one metre tall and looks like a small hydrangea. Its attractive blue flowers and fruit can be seen from the Three Kings Islands south to Rakitu.

Some of the daisies include sneezeweed (*Centipeda minima*), a tiny annual herb of wet areas, known only in the Auckland region from Great Barrier (Whangapoua), Little Barrier and Kawau Islands. Three button daisies (*Leptinella* spp.) have been recorded. One is now thought to be extinct (*L. squalida*), and the other two (*L. tenella* and *L. dioica*) are quite local. The attractive coastal daisy *Celmisia major* var. *major* was thought to be extinct on Great Barrier but was recently rediscovered.

Three herbs presumed extinct are *Atriplex hollowayi*, shore spurge (*Euphorbia glauca*) and *Vittadinia australis*. *A. hollowayi*, a low-growing annual, grew on Great Barrier's exposed eastern beaches and was present in Kirk's time. Shore spurge is an erect perennial herb that grows up to a metre high, often in sand dunes, and was last seen on Great Barrier in the 1970s. It has generally declined in its northern New Zealand habitats. *V. australis,* a small daisy of open places, once reached its northern geographical limit on Great Barrier, where Kirk collected it on Kaikoura Island.

ORCHIDS (48 SPECIES)

One of these, a robust wetland orchid (*Prasophyllum* aff. *patens*), is known only from Kirk's collections from the Kaitoke wetland. Other orchids known from this wetland include *Spiranthes novae-zelandiae*, which has bright pink flowers on spiralled stems, and a sun orchid, *Thelymitra formosa*. In 1997 a new orchid for Great Barrier, *Prasophyllum* aff. *colensoi*, with greenish-yellow flowers, was also found in the Kaitoke wetland.

Three unusual orchids are the potato orchids *Gastrodia cunninghamii* and *G.* aff. *sesamoides*, with brownish stems and flowers and potato-like underground tubers; and a tiny forest orchid, *Danhatchia australis,* whose short, pinkish, flowering stems occur during summer in almost pure taraire

Danhatchia australis at Te Paparahi. Seeing an open flower like this is unusual.

Ewen Cameron

Orthocerus novae-zelandiae at Te Paparahi.

Ewen Cameron

forest. These are all saprophytic; that is, they feed on decaying matter (like fungi) and do not require light.

Great Barrier's summer-flowering sun orchids, *Thelymitra* (nine species) and *Orthocerus novae-zelandica*, grow mainly on sunny clay banks. The island's spider orchids (*Corybas*, six species) and greenhoods (*Pterostylis*, eight species) occur in shady forest.

GRASSES, SEDGES, LILIES, ETC (119 SPECIES)

Two renga lilies (*Arthropodium* spp.) are present on Great Barrier. The smaller one (*A. candidum*) is rather local and reaches its northern geographical limit at Te Paparahi. The large epiphytic tank lilies (*Astelia* and *Collospermum* spp.) are common on the island, except for *C. microspermum*, which occurs only by Tataweka. The smallest native member of the iris family, *Libertia pulchella*, is common by Mt Hobson, where its white flowers stand out in early summer. Two larger members of this genus (*L. grandiflora* and *L. pulchella*) grow elsewhere on the island.

Spring-flowering *Corybas rivularis* is one of six spider orchids found on the island.

Ewen Cameron

A tank lily, *Collospermum microspermum*, at Tataweka has a restricted distribution, unlike its widespread close relative, *C. hastatum*, which has wider leaves. Male flowers.

Ewen Cameron

Sand tussock with golden-coloured pingao, eastern Great Barrier. Disturbance has probably caused this species to decrease.

Ewen Cameron

Of the 54 sedges recorded, several are quite scarce. The following genera are well represented: *Carex* (16 species), *Baumea* (6), *Isolepis* (5), *Schoenus* (5), *Uncinia* (5) and *Gahnia* (4). The tiny leafless sedge *Eleocharis neozelandica* was discovered in 1999 on one of the east coast beaches, where it appears to have recently become established. It is known from North Cape to Farewell Spit, but is absent from large areas of the North Island coast. The collection of the Australasian swamp sedge (*Schoenus carsei*), in 1980, from near Claris, appears to be one of few New Zealand records of this plant in the last 50 years. The Australasian burr-weed (*Sparganium subglobosum*) occurs in the Kaitoke wetland.

Thirty native grasses have been recorded from Great Barrier, and include four unusual species. Karetu or scented grass (*Hierochloe redolens*) has broad leaves and flowering stems more than a metre high. It was recorded only by Kirk and occurs from the Three Kings Islands to southern South Island, but is uncommon in the northern part of its range. Maori had many uses for its scented leaves. The tiny splash-zone *Zoysia minima* is only known from the northern tip of Te Paparahi. Australasian sand tussock (*Austrofestuca littoralis*) grows on the east coast beaches, the site of the grass's last colonies in the Auckland region. It often grows with two other native sand-binding species, spinifex (*Spinifex sericeus*) and pingao (*Desmoeschoenus spiralis*). *Amphibromus fluitans*, a swamp species, is known on the island only from a single collection near Claris in 1989. Owing to swamp drainage and competition from weeds, this Australasian plant is now a threatened species in New Zealand.

ABSENCES AND ADDITIONS

The most notable absence is hard beech (*Nothofagus truncata*), which is present on other Hauraki Gulf islands (Little Barrier, Waiheke, Ponui, Kawau) and parts of Coromandel, Auckland and Northland. Because beech seeds are not blown far from the parent tree, and sink in sea water, beech requires a land connection to disperse. Its absence suggests that either it died out, or that it spread through the Hauraki Gulf after Great Barrier last separated from the mainland. (See also box, p.85, for species present on the summit of Little Barrier and Mt Moehau but oddly absent from Mt Hobson/Hirakimata.)

Great Barrier is a relatively large island, suggesting many more native plants may yet be discovered. The wood rose (*Dactylanthus taylorii*) is one possibility. Others with a good means of dispersal may yet arrive or return without human assistance (for example, orchids and ferns). Three plants recorded on the summits of Little Barrier and Mt Moehau (*Dracophyllum traversii, Griselina littoralis, Peraxilla tetrapetala*) are surprisingly absent from Great Barrier. Some species presumed to be extinct will no doubt be rediscovered, while others will require human assistance to return.

INTRODUCED PLANTS

A complete list has not yet been compiled of the naturalised species, but there are several hundred of them. Most are herbaceous and form a minor part of the vegetation. Naturalised plants usually establish themselves in the wild through dispersal from garden ornamentals, but fortunately Great Barrier's small resident population means there are few such gardens. Only some 10 percent of the naturalised species are considered to have a major negative impact on the native vegetation; that is, to merit the name 'weeds'. The best weed control is prevention; established Hauraki Gulf weeds like rhamnus (*Rhamnus alaternus*) are so far unrecorded.

Pampas grass surrounds the quarry, shedding its wind-blown seed into the freshly crushed rock, to be distributed with the road metal around the island.

Ewen Cameron

Among the well-established weeds are pampas grasses (*Cortaderia jubata* and *C. selloana*), dally pine (*Psoralea pinnata*), Mexican devil (*Ageratina adenophora*) and mist flower (*A. riparia*). Wildling pines (*Pinus pinaster* and *P. radiata*) are conspicuous in some southern areas, and wattles (*Acacia* spp.) are increasing. Hakea (*Hakea gibbosa* and *H. sericea*) and heathers (*Erica baccans* and *E. lusitanica*) are common in the manuka shrublands, but natural regeneration in the absence of fire should largely shade them out. The aggressive coastal grasses kikuyu (*Pennisetum clandestinum*), buffalo (*Stenotaphrum secundatum*) and marram (*Ammophila arenaria*) are present and difficult to control. Oxygen weed (*Egeria densa*), found in the golf course pond, threatened the outstanding Kaitoke wetland, but has almost been eradicated. Sweet-grass reed (*Glyceria maxima*), a luxuriant aquatic grass present near Okiwi, also threatens wetlands. Fortunately, woolly nightshade (*Solanum mauritianum*), which is common on the mainland and Waiheke Island, is very local on Great Barrier and should be eradicated before it spreads.

Many other weeds exist in local populations, especially near habitation. Examples include wandering Jew (*Tradescantia fluminensis*), polygala (*Polygala myrtifolia*), Kahili ginger (*Hedychium gardnerianum*), Mexican daisy (*Erigeron karvinskianus*), climbing asparagus (*Asparagus scandens*), smilax (*A. asparagoides*), periwinkle (*Vinca major*), moth plant (*Araujia sericifera*), jasmine (*Jasminum*

A native pigeon eating strawberry guavas in a Port Fitzroy garden. Will this become a weed here as it has on Norfolk Island?

Ewen Cameron

polyanthum), ivy (*Hedera helix*), coast banksia (*Banksia integrifolia*) and Japanese honeysuckle (*Lonicera japonica*). Unless controlled, these weeds will spread and compromise the value of the indigenous flora. Some fruit trees could prove to be a problem in the future; for example, strawberry guava (*Psidum cattleianum*), loquat (*Eriobotrya japonica*), olive (*Olea europaea*) and ornamental cherries (*Prunus* spp.).

Low-climbing but smothering, climbing asparagus is perhaps the worst forest weed of northern New Zealand. Fortunately it is still very local on Great Barrier.

Ewen Cameron

PROTECTION AND CONSERVATION

Fortunately nearly two-thirds of Great Barrier and its outliers is in public ownership and managed for its outstanding flora and fauna values. This encompasses most of the major natural areas except for some of the forested islands, particularly Kaikoura and Nelson. However, natural habitats continue to be degraded or lost, particularly through browsing by exotic mammals. Regeneration of palatable species — for example, koromiko (*Hebe* spp.) and toropapa (*Alseuosmia* spp.) — was virtually non-existent in Te Paparahi until feral goats were severely reduced in the late 1980s. Rats eating the seed and seedlings of coastal milk tree (*Streblus banksii*), parapara or bird-catching tree (*Pisonia brunoniana*) and coastal mahoe are probably the reason that today these species are virtually restricted to a few of the surrounding islands. The extinction of *Atriplex hollowayi* was possibly due to rabbit browsing, and pigs possibly caused the extinction of king fern, last seen in the 1880s.

Will this low native herb, *Leptinella dioica,* ultimately be smothered to extinction on the island by kikuyu or buffalo grass?

Ewen Cameron

Competition from weeds is ongoing. Indigenous herbaceous species that grow in the open will come under increasing pressure as existing weeds build up and spread and new ones establish. Low herbs such as willowherbs (*Epilobium* spp.), creeping fuchsia, button daisies (*Leptinella* spp.), native carrot (*Daucus glochidiatus*), *Amphibromus fluitans* and *Ranunculus urvilleanus* are at risk. Possible early Polynesian introductions to New Zealand such as *Sigesbeckia orientalis*, cobbler's pegs (*Bidens pilosa*) and *Paspalum orbiculare* now only survive in more remote places like Great Barrier, where competition with other weeds is less. An alternative to planting exotics that may later naturalise is to plant indigenous species. However, to protect the local gene stock, such plantings should be sourced from island stock.

Two natives appear to be in danger of being swamped by hybridisation with another native species. They are the Great Barrier kanuka (crossing with the common kanuka) and the threatened fireweed (*Senecio scaberulus*) crossing with *S. hispidulus*. Some plants appear to depend on coastal animal colonies (for example, seabirds, seals and sea lions) to provide the heavily fertilised environment they require. Cook's scurvy grass and *Rorippa divaricata* are two such species, and are now absent from the main island. The future of these species may depend on the restoration of the animal populations.

Great Barrier has the advantage of being an island, which makes it easier to control weeds and animal pests and stop new ones from establishing. The prevention of fires is also important. After being severely damaged by land clearances in the past, most of Great Barrier's natural vegetation is today regenerating strongly, and this offers hope for the future.

CHAPTER SIX

LAND AND FRESHWATER
INVERTEBRATES

About five thousand species of land and freshwater invertebrates (animals without backbones) are thought to live on Great Barrier and its outlying islands. There has been little research done on the island's fauna, so there is much yet to discover. From what is known, relationships exist between the invertebrate fauna of Great Barrier and that of the Coromandel Peninsula and Northland, and to a lesser extent that of the Auckland isthmus and other offshore islands. Few of Great Barrier's invertebrates are endemic to the island.

These animals range from tiny, microscopic protozoa (for example, amoebas), rotifers, nematodes (eelworms) and a range of small annelids (worms) that live in the soil and fresh water, to large animals such as stick insects, cave wetas, freshwater crayfish and the giant earthworm. Some are parasitic in or on the outside of other animals, such as the tiny wasps that are parasitic on caterpillars, and mites that live on the bodies of native bees.

The majority of Great Barrier's invertebrates are insects. Few species are exotic to New Zealand, and these include pests such as wasps, fleas and lice.

Prospects are decidedly favourable for the continued survival of Great Barrier's native invertebrates because the island is free of the vertebrate pests ranging from possums, stoats, ferrets and Norway rats, to mosquito fish (*Gambusia*), which have done so much damage elsewhere in New Zealand. It also helps that the forest is rapidly regenerating.

INSECTS

Streams and other freshwater areas provide habitats for the larvae of groups such as mayflies, caddisflies, stoneflies, dragonflies and damselflies, as well as for the larvae of mosquitoes and sandflies. Other species of fly live in a range of habitats; their larvae generally feed on decaying vegetation, dung, dead animals and rotting seaweed, and in so doing play an important role in cleaning up the environment.

The biodiversity of freshwater insects has remained high because Great Barrier has only native freshwater fish such as kokopu and eels; there are no acclimatised fish like trout. This diversity is particularly evident in the upper catchments where forests have been less affected by early logging of kauri.

Studies of the mayflies have revealed 24 species on Great Barrier, a diversity comparable to areas in the Auckland region. While no endemic mayflies are known, it does have the rare fringe-gilled mayfly, *Isothraulus abditus*.

Beetles are by far the largest group of insects on the island, but most of the species present are tiny and not so obvious. Their food sources range from rotten wood to the leaves and roots of plants, and to other invertebrates; for example, some ladybirds are predators on aphids and mites.

An undescribed species of flightless ground beetle has been found under stones in low-altitude native forest near Rosalie Bay. This beetle, a species of *Mecodema*, is related to other ground beetles found in Coromandel and Northland. Ground beetles are predators on insect larvae, slugs and other animals that live in leaf litter.

The carabid beetle *Mecodema*, a flightless ground beetle possibly endemic to Great Barrier Island. One of approximately 60 species throughout New Zealand.

Len Doel

Larvae and adults of the sand scarab (*Pericoptus truncatus*) are found under logs and vegetation on sandy beaches. The adult is a large black beetle and its larva is a large, fleshy grub up to 60 mm long. Captain Thomas Broun,

Sand scarab beetle. Up to 25 mm long, it can quickly burrow into the sand.

Len Doel

Sand scarab larva. Found in the sandhills back from the shore, this large fleshy grub feeds on plant roots.

Len Doel

an army captain and one of New Zealand's pioneer entomologists, discovered and named a related species, *P. nitidulus*, from Great Barrier in 1880. Despite several searches, it has not been found since.

Other beetles of note include the small, light-brown chafer beetle (*Sericospilus watti*), huhu beetle and hister beetle (*Tomogenius latipes*). The chafer beetle has so far been found only on Great Barrier Island. Its larvae feed on plant roots. Huhu beetles, members of the long-horn beetle family and New Zealand's largest beetle, occur throughout Great Barrier. The larvae feed in rotten trees, such as kauri, rimu, kahikatea and pine, are edible and an important traditional food of the Maori. The small shiny black hister beetle has been found in the guano of short-tailed bats on Little Barrier, and in the nests of black-backed gulls and kingfishers on Great Barrier.

Bugs include the green vegetable bug (*Nezara viridula*), a pest of vegetables, and also native species that suck the sap from fruits, seeds and leaves; they include bugs that prey on caterpillars, aphids and the like. Great Barrier has its share of pests that feed by sucking the sap from plants, including aphids, scale insects, mealybugs and whiteflies. There are a few native termites which feed on wood, ants that form colonies in the soil, and grasshoppers, crickets and wetas, which feed mainly on vegetable matter, dead or alive.

The giant cave weta, *Gymnoplectron acanthocera*, is particularly notable. On Great Barrier it lives in mineshafts, caves, crevices and holes in trees — even in household water tanks. This weta has a short body but long legs and antennae so that the total length of the animal may reach 35 cm. Each antenna is made up of more than 550 tiny segments, and the animal's large hind legs enable it to jump and scurry with great agility. Cave wetas often gather in clusters on the walls of caves, particularly near seepages. They feed on decaying organic material. There is some evidence that cave wetas come out of the caves to feed at night, but this observation may relate to populations living in shallow crevices and tree-holes away from caves and tunnels.

Cave weta. This harmless weta lives in damp holes or crevices, and very often caves, feeding on decaying organic matter.

Len Doel

Among other wetas reported from Great Barrier is the giant weta or wetapunga, *Deinacrida heteracantha*. An unconfirmed sighting 15 years ago suggests this 'invertebrate mouse' may yet be living on Great Barrier, otherwise it may be restricted to Little Barrier Island.

Native bees are solitary but often nest together in holes in clay banks. Wasps include the larger introduced species, such as the German (*Vespula germanica*) and the paper (*Polistes chinensis*), which make colonial nests. Wasps also include predatory species which hunt a range of insects and spiders, such as the native mason wasp (*Pison spinolae*), which preys on orb-web spiders, using them to provision its clay nests. There are also hundreds of parasitic wasps that lay their eggs inside caterpillars and larvae. The eggs hatch into parasitic larvae which feed inside these animals.

Like most of New Zealand, Great Barrier has only a few types of butterfly. The introduced white butterfly *(Pieris rapae)*, whose caterpillar feeds on cabbage and garden nasturtium, is often seen through the summer months, as is the monarch butterfly *(Danaus plexippus)*. The monarch is a native of North America. Its caterpillars depend solely on the exotic swan plant for survival.

Other butterflies include the tiny common blue, seen flying among grass and whose caterpillars feed on clover, trefoil and medic; and two species of copper butterfly, the common copper *Lycaena salustius* and Rauparaha's copper (*Lycaena rauparaha*), the larvae of which feed on the leaves of pohuehue (*Muehlenbeckia*). The adults are both coppery coloured with black lines and dots and have a wingspan of up to 35 mm.

Yellow admiral or kahu. Regularly seen about the island, this native is also possibly a migrant from Australia. It has a 45-55mm wingspan and may sometimes be seen gathered in groups above open hilltops. A strong flyer.

Mavis Lessiter

Admiral butterflies, both red and yellow, occur regularly on Great Barrier Island. The yellow admiral, *Bassaris itea*, is slightly smaller than the red, has prominent yellow patches in the middle of the upper side of its forewing and is a well-known migratory species, particularly in Australia.

The red admiral or kahukura ('red cloak'), *Bassaris gonerilla*, is native to New Zealand. It has a distinctive black-and-red colouring and a large red patch on the upper side of each wing. Its larvae feed on the tree nettle, ongaonga or (as is the case with the yellow) the introduced *Urtica urens* (stinging nettle) and *U. incisa* (a native nettle related to ongaonga). However, none of these nettles has been found on Great Barrier Island. The nearest place for ongaonga, is the Coromandel Peninsula and for *U. urens*, the inner gulf islands and Auckland mainland. The regular occurrence of admirals on Great Barrier reflects their ability to fly long distances and over water.

New Zealand has more than 1,800 species of moths, mostly native, and Great Barrier has its fair share of these. In swamps or wetlands on the eastern side of the island there are tiny, 5 mm black and silver moths (*Glyphipterix* spp.) whose caterpillars are specialised to bore inside the stems

Red admiral or kahukura. Camouflaged butterfly at rest, when it may open its wings to reveal the large red flashes possibly used to discourage predatory birds.

Mavis Lessiter

Yellow admiral. The larvae of both the yellow and red admiral feed on nettles, which so far have not been found on Great Barrier. Larvae are also attacked by parasitic wasps.

Mavis Lessiter

of wetland rushes and reeds. At the other end of the scale is the giant puriri moth, with a wingspan of 150 mm. Its caterpillars live for many years inside holes in tree trunks, not just of puriri but also putaputaweta. Once the caterpillar has finished with the hole, tree weta take up residence, hence the Maori name, which means 'many wetas'. The adult stage of the puriri moth is short-lived, as it has no mouth with

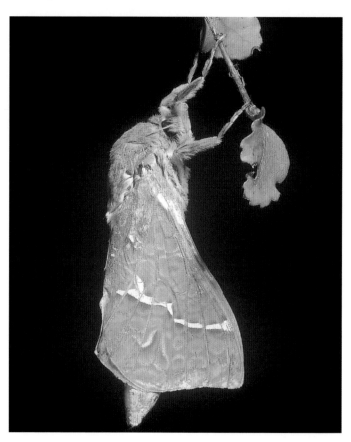

Male puriri moth. New Zealand's largest native moth. The caterpillar stage may spend up to six years in a hole it has burrowed into the trunk of the puriri, its main host tree. After the moth emerges from the pupa stage, a scar forms on the tree. The female moth is larger than the male and duller in colour.

Len Doel

Glow-worms. Light attracts small flying prey to become caught on the sticky lines along which the glow-worm larvae move to the attack. A common sight at night along bush tracks on the island.

Len Doel

which to feed. The males are bright green and can be attracted to light; the females are green and mottled brown, and are very rarely seen.

Another insect of note is the New Zealand glow-worm,which is found on the banks of the streams on Great Barrier, as well as on banks in damp areas throughout the bush. The light is only produced by the larva, from a chemical reaction in the rear part of the body. The adult fly is a type of fungus-feeding gnat.

Brown stick insect. Masters of camouflage, they will rock rhythmically when touched or disturbed to further confound potential predators. They are active night feeders on leaves.

Len Doel

At least three species of stick insect have been found on Great Barrier. The smooth stick insect, *Clitarchus hookeri*, is widespread, often on manuka or kanuka. It is generally green and very well camouflaged. Another species of *Clitarchus* is brown with small spines along the sides of its thorax. It may be a new species, and most resembles a type that is so far only known from the Three Kings Islands. The third species is the large black-spined stick insect *Acanthoxyla prasina*, reaching up to 11 cm long and usually bright green (sometimes brown) in colour. All stick insects feed on leaves, and are often more active at night.

The green stick insect has red patches on its front legs to surprise bird or reptile predators.

Len Doel

BATS — INVERTEBRATE FEEDERS

A number of Great Barrier's invertebrate animals are preyed on by New Zealand's only terrestrial mammals — bats. Flying insects form the main diet of the long-tailed bat (*Chalinolobus tuberculatus*), while non-flying insects, centipedes, millipedes, spiders and larvae, along with pollen, nectar and fruit, attract the lesser short-tailed bat (*Mystacina tuberculata*).

The long-tailed bat is a member of a large, widespread family. It is thought to have arrived here from Australia about one million years ago and is widely distributed throughout New Zealand, although large numbers occur in only a few areas. Long-tailed bats come out at dusk to feed, and may be seen at this time flying over farmland near the edge of a forest or around remnant stands of trees. They are fast, highly manoeuvrable fliers like the fantail and swallow.

The lesser short-tailed bat is the only remaining member of a family endemic to New Zealand. Its closest

The short-tailed bat weighs around 12 g and has a 28 cm wingspan. Its short, velvety fur is golden brown. Its tail is short and protrudes above the tail membrane. A blind, wingless batfly lives in the roosts of short-tailed bats and is sometimes found clinging to their fur. Short-tailed bat roosts have been found only in native trees.

Alina Arkins

Long-tailed bat. This bat weighs around 9 g and has a wingspan of approximately 25 cm. The fur is a chocolate-brown colour. They have a tail almost as long as their body. They roost in both native and exotic trees, caves and, rarely, buildings. Females of both species of bat gather in large maternity roosts in early summer, where the young are born.

Len Doel

relative, the greater short-tailed bat, is thought to be extinct. The short-tailed bat is believed to be a relic of Gondwana, and to have been isolated in New Zealand for the past 30 million years. Recent research suggests that they are most closely related to a South American bat species. Short-tailed bats are found on Little Barrier Island and were historically recorded on Coromandel Peninsula in forest similar to that in parts of Great Barrier. It is at least a possibility that a remnant population may live on the island.

Short-tailed bats have perhaps the widest-ranging diet of any bat, catching prey in the air, on the ground and probably on vegetation. They possess strong hind legs and wings that fold up tightly, enabling them to move easily on the forest litter. Their known distribution is restricted to native forest.

Both New Zealand bat species are echo-locators, which means they use sonar pulses to navigate and catch their prey. They are most active over the summer months. When it gets colder they lower their metabolic rate and become torpid, but may rouse themselves occasionally, perhaps to take advantage of a warmer night to feed.

EARTHWORMS AND FLATWORMS

Large earthworms are frequently found under stones and logs or burrowing in the leaf litter. They belong to the family Megascolecidae, some of which are enormous. For example, the giant *Celeriella gigantea* (formerly *Spenceriella*) can reach 1.4 metres in length. These construct long burrows through the soil and deep into the clay, and depend on forest cover as they feed by taking forest leaf litter down into their burrows. At least six other species are known from Great Barrier, mostly 150 to 200 mm long.

Giant earthworm. These worms may burrow several metres down into the clay. Little is known of their reproductive habits. They are fragile and easily damaged.

Len Doel

Introduced earthworms, found in compost heaps and gardens, include the tiger worm, *Eisenia*, used in composting toilets. The large flatworm seen regularly on the island is a predator on these earthworms, but little more is known about it than this.

SLUGS AND SNAILS

One of the more unusual species is the native paua slug, *Schizoglossa novoseelandica barrierensis*, which grows to 100 mm long and is named for the small thin opaque paua-like shell on its back. The animal itself is grey-black in colour and lives under stones and logs and among forest litter. Paua slugs are carnivores and feed on earthworms and other slugs and snails. They lay quite large white eggs about 4 mm in diameter, under logs and in leaf litter.

Paua slug. This slug is named for the paua-like shell on its back. It feeds on smaller soil animals and often hunts out worms in their burrows. It lays a few large white eggs in the damp litter under a log or stone.

Len Doel

There is some debate as to whether this is a subspecies of the same paua slug found elsewhere in New Zealand, and therefore endemic to Great Barrier. The related species and other relatives have been found in various parts of the North Island, ranging from Hokianga in the north to Wanganui in the south. Sub-fossil remains of *Schizoglossa* species have been found, often associated with moa bones, in the Waikato, at Gisborne, Waikaremoana, near Nuhaka in Hawke's Bay and at Mt Hikurangi, East Cape. This type of slug probably represents a line of animals that evolved along with the New Zealand giant land snails, and that probably specialised in crawling through earthworm burrows in hunt of their prey.

A number of small land snails have been found on the island. There is also the large flax snail or pupuharakeke, *Placostylus hongii*. Its status on the island is unknown but this snail is of conservation significance, as many of its mainland colonies are now extinct.

OTHER ARTHROPODS

A wide range of other joint-legged animals are found on Great Barrier, including crustaceans, centipedes, millipedes and arachnids. The freshwater crayfish or koura is generally found in fast-running, stony-bottomed parts of streams. The shrimp *Paratya* is found in slower parts of streams with

The giant centipede or weri preys on a variety of small animals. Its bite can leave a painful reminder to be more careful next time. It can grow up to 225 mm long.

Len Doel

marginal vegetation. Sand hoppers also occur under stones and rotten wood and are often the first animals to be seen when a log is turned over as they jump and scurry for cover. Here also are woodlice or slaters that feed on rotting organic matter. The common centipede or weri, *Cormocephalus*, is found under stones and logs and behind the loose leaf-bases of nikau palm. It reaches 225 mm long and 10 mm wide,

and is dark reddish brown with a shiny blue-violet tinge. Centipedes prey on smaller animals – slaters, beetle larvae and sand hoppers. They need to be handled with care, as their large jaws can piece the skin, creating a bite that can be very sore for up to two weeks.

The arachnids include several groups of predators — spiders, harvestmen, false scorpions and some mites — but little is known about most of these on Great Barrier.

Tunnelweb spider. Silken threads extending into the leaf-litter from its tunnel alert this spider to attack the unlucky victim.

Len Doel

False katipo spider. Rapidly displacing our native katipo spider, this South African immigrant can deliver a painful bite. Found under stones and logs.

Len Doel

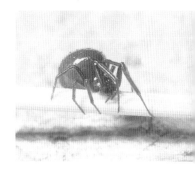

As on the nearby mainland, there are many different types of spider on Great Barrier. The large tunnelweb spider, *Porrhothele*, constructs a tunnel of silk under logs and loose bark. Any small animal disturbing the silken lines extending from the tunnel is rapidly attacked. The false katipo, *Steatoda*, a small, round, glossy black species, introduced from southern Africa, is found under stones and logs. Like the katipo, which it is displacing in many parts of New Zealand, it can deliver a nasty bite. Another species with a painful bite is the white-tailed spider, (*Lampona murina*) an introduction from Australia. This spider is frequently found on the walls of houses. Its preferred prey is other spiders.

PERIPATUS

Peripatus is classified as a 'missing link' related to both worms (Annelida) and joint-legged animals (Arthropoda), and so belongs to its own phylum, the Onychophora. These animals live under logs and feed on small insects. Peripatus feeds by first 'spitting' out a sticky mass in front of its head to trap its prey. The presence of peripatus on Great Barrier was recently confirmed.

Peripatus. This 'missing link' between worms and arthropods was recently found on Great Barrier. It has a velvety skin, hence the common name of velvet worm. It spits a sticky mass at its prey to entrap them.

Len Doel

117

CHAPTER SEVEN

REPTILES AND FROGS

Compared to other islands in the Hauraki Gulf and the adjacent North Island mainland, Great Barrier supports an extremely wide range of reptiles, including eight species of native skink and five of native gecko. There may also be three other species of native skink and the rare tuatara. There are also two frog species, one introduced and one native. In comparison the Auckland area has five skinks, three geckos and one frog (all native) and most nearby islands have up to six lizard species. Only neighbouring Little Barrier Island and some of the nearby Mercury Islands support a comparable variety.

There are a number of reasons why Great Barrier has such a wealth of reptiles. First, the island's past land bridges to Coromandel and Northland provided dispersal pathways for animals to and from Great Barrier. When Great Barrier was cut off from the mainland, a cross-section of mainland species remained. Second, Great Barrier's large size and diverse ecosystems enable the island to support many species. Third, despite its history of forest clearance and logging, the island retains considerable forest cover, and shoreline habitats remain relatively intact.

Introduced browsers and predators, however, are a threat. Goats, pigs and wandering cattle browse understorey plants, reducing ground cover such as ferns and compacting leaf litter that provides shelter and food for reptiles. Introduced browsers also degrade habitat – especially frog habitat – by fouling waterways and increasing erosion and siltation of streams. Ship rats, Pacific rats (kiore) and mice all prey on lizards. Pigs elsewhere have been recorded eating lizards, and also destroy habitat such as stone piles and fern patches when rooting for food.

Cats are a major threat, and in the island's remote areas the problem is not only feral cats: studies elsewhere show that domestic cats are very wide-ranging, and may travel more than 10 kilometres from their homes to hunt.

Ironically, domestic cats on the island have helped provide conservation managers with information on the distribution of the threatened chevron skink (*Oligosoma homalonotum*) by bringing home their catch, but they must eat many more lizards than are seen by their owners. Threats to lizards will be even greater if animals like Norway rats, mustelids and possums reach the island. Whereas ship rats prefer dry areas, Norway rats frequent wet places, especially habitats thought to be important to chevron skinks. Mustelids such as stoats and ferrets are voracious predators of lizards and other wildlife, and the introduction of these to the island would create an ecological crisis.

LIZARDS

Lizards are present all over Great Barrier. Most of these species are nocturnal, and those that are active during the day are relatively timid. Geckos are distinguished from skinks by their very smooth skin, which is almost velvety (owing to very small scales), pads of skin under the toes to assist climbing, and the ability to lick their eyes, which, unlike those of skinks, do not have a movable eyelid and hence cannot blink.

Up to four species of skink and two of gecko can be found in shoreline habitats. Most easily seen are the copper skink (*Cyclodina aenea*), which is active at dawn and dusk, the moko skink (*Oligosoma moco*) and the shore skink (*O. smithi*) (both active by day).

Copper skinks are the smallest native lizard. They have a bronze back, brown sides flecked with black and white, and a cream or yellowish-cream unspotted belly. The throat is usually heavily spotted with black, and the tail, especially the underside, may be flushed with red. Copper skinks rarely emerge from the scrub cover at the back of the beach.

Moko skinks are slightly larger than copper skinks. (Moko is the Maori word for lizard.) This species has a chocolate-brown back and a darker brown longitudinal 'racing' stripe edged with white running down each side. A few specimens are very dark, almost black, and may have an X-shaped mark on the head. They are quite conspicuous if you sit on the margin of the shore vegetation on sunny days; and will often come close. Both copper and moko skinks feed on small invertebrates, and moko skinks have been known to eat jam from the hand. The copper skink is found in good numbers on the island, but the moko is endangered.

Inhabitants of the shoreline, shore skinks are conspicuous by day as they bask among rocks or forage in seaweed mats. On islands free of introduced predators shore skinks reach enormous numbers, showing what Great Barrier beaches must once have looked like.

Len Doel

Further towards the tidal zone, the shore skink inhabits boulder banks, driftwood and vegetation mats, and forages for decaying matter washed up in the tide, and beach arthropods. The shore skink has a very pointed snout, is heavily speckled in shades of dark grey, brown or green, and its belly may be grey, cream-coloured, reddish or black. Some specimens are entirely black, and some may have weak stripes or a lightly spotted belly. Shore skinks can often be seen basking where the sun penetrates boulder banks, and their dark bodies contrast vividly with the surrounding rocks.

Less conspicuous lizards of the shoreline include the nocturnal egg-laying skink (*Oligosoma suteri*), which has an almost black body. Its undersurface is greyish or occasionally pink or bright orange. The egg-laying skink takes its name from the fact that it is the only native lizard to lay eggs. Several females may share a nest under big stones in hollows in silt, sand or gravel. The shore and egg-laying skinks are endangered.

The geckos that inhabit Great Barrier's shoreline are the Duvaucel's gecko (*Hoplodactylus duvaucelii*) and the common gecko (*H. maculatus*). These nocturnal animals generally hide by day under driftwood or clumps of vegetation, emerging at night to feed on nectar, fruit, and arthropods such as spiders and insects. They do, however, occasionally sunbask. Duvaucel's gecko is New Zealand's largest living lizard and one of the largest geckos in the world. It has a heavy body and its toes have expanded pads. In colour it is mainly grey, often with a faint olive-green hue. This gecko is very rare, if not extinct, on the island.

The smaller common gecko is likely to be found throughout coastal areas of the island. The grey or brown colour of its upper sides exhibits complex irregular markings that may include patches of black, white, yellow-orange and olive-green. These markings usually run across the body, but some have longitudinal stripes. The belly is pale and usually unspotted.

A wider range of lizards is to be found in inland than shoreline areas, although many of the species have very localised distribution. The copper skink is widespread throughout the island's forest and shrublands, as is the ornate skink (*Cyclodina ornata*). This species is similar in colour but slightly larger than the copper skink, and has

By far New Zealand's largest gecko, the Duvaucel's gecko is both arboreal and ground-dwelling. On Great Barrier Duvaucel's geckos are most likely to be found in the canopy of mature forest areas, away from predators such as rats and cats. Well-developed claws and wide toe pads enable all geckos to climb vertical surfaces.

Len Doel

large, pale blotches along the top and sides of its tail. It can also be distinguished from the copper skink by the white or yellowish 'teardrop' edged with black below each eye. It is occasionally found down to the edge of the shore.

Great Barrier's forests also support three nationally significant species of skink. The marbled skink (*Cyclodina oliveri*) is restricted to only a handful of northern offshore islands, and on Great Barrier it has been recorded only in the northern block, in low numbers. Likewise the striped skink (*Oligosoma striatum*), small and pale brown with a striking putty-coloured line running from snout to tail on either side of its back, is locally restricted on the North Island mainland. To date, only one individual has been found on each of Great and Little Barrier Islands. This skink seems to prefer rotting fallen logs or epiphytes on canopy trees. Protection and maturation of forests on Great Barrier will ensure greater areas of suitable habitat for it in the future.

The third skink, the chevron, has attracted considerable attention over recent years and is arguably the lizard with which most Great Barrier residents identify. Found only on Great Barrier and neighbouring Little Barrier Island, this reddish-brown lizard is named for the distinctive light and dark patches that form a row of chevron markings down its back and tail. It is one of New Zealand's largest native skinks.

Great Barrier is one of only two islands that support the highly endangered chevron skink. Found throughout the island in low numbers and under threat from feral and domestic cats, little is known of its ecology and habits -— but research under way should provide information and hope for its continued survival.

Len Doel

Only a single individual has ever been found on Little Barrier Island, so Great Barrier is the primary focus for conservation efforts. This skink is widespread throughout the island but typically in very low densities: only 100 or so have ever been reported. They have been found from the northern block to Mt Hobson (Hirakimata), Whangaparapara, Okupu and Tryphena. Little is known about the ecology and habitat needs of the species, but the Department of Conservation aims at carrying out the necessary research.

All five gecko species on the island use forest areas and are live principally in trees. Duvaucel's gecko and the common gecko also favour, as previously mentioned, shoreline habitats. Duvaucel's gecko is very rare in either of these habitats, but the common gecko is found throughout mature and regenerating forest. The forest gecko (*Hoplodactylus granulatus*) is known from sightings mostly in the south-east of the island. It is grey-brown or reddish brown, with black and white and occasional yellowish patches. Its back has a series of large, irregular transverse blotches. A bright white band runs from each eye to ear, the belly is heavily blotched and the feet have yellow soles. Although nocturnal, it may sunbask.

The gecko that tends to be seen most readily on the island is the Pacific gecko (*H. pacificus*), which often appears

Above: Perfectly coloured to blend in with its arboreal forest habitat, the forest gecko is only found in southern parts of Great Barrier. One or two young are born live in mid to late summer. Although mainly nocturnal, these geckos may bask outside their refuges in tree branches or under loose bark.

Len Doel

Below: Both arboreal and ground-dwelling, the Pacific gecko is most readily seen at night on clay banks along the island's roads. Road cuttings offer warm places with deep cracks as retreats. The dark brown and grey patches that run across the back are similar to those of the common gecko.

Len Doel

The emerald green skin of the common green gecko blends perfectly with the native scrub and forest in which it lives. These geckos are active by day, but their coloration and arboreal nature makes them hard to see. They are less inclined than other lizards to shed their tails, probably because they are so important in aiding climbing.

Len Doel

at night around the cracked clay banks of road cuttings. In colouring it is similar to but somewhat brighter than the common gecko. When resting, the Pacific gecko has a more alert-looking posture than the common gecko.

These four geckos are nocturnal. The green gecko (*Naultinus e. elegans*), however, is diurnal and is found in low numbers in the island's manuka scrub and forest interiors. It has distinctively bright green skin, a dark blue mouth lining and blue tongue. Occasional specimens are bright yellow, a colour form probably analogous to the albino in other animals. The green gecko uses its slim tail like an extra 'foot' to aid movement through foliage.

FROGS

The only native frog on the island, Hochstetter's frog (*Leiopelma hochstetteri*), is rarely seen because of its cryptic brown coloration, small size and need for unmodified streams under native forest. It has only ever been found in the remote northern block, and even there its future is uncertain given the effects of introduced predators and browsers. More widespread is the introduced southern bell frog (*Litoria raniformis*), with its conspicuous green and gold

More suited to pristine forest than modified scrub or farmland, Hochstetter's frog is the small silent native cousin of the much larger and more vocal golden bell frog, an introduced species. Unlike introduced frogs, the young of Hochstetter's and other native frogs develop inside their eggs and emerge as tailed froglets.

Len Doel

coloration. Individuals are readily found in wet areas like the Kaitoke Swamp, low-lying pasture or in the damp hollows behind sand dunes; for example, at Okiwi and Kaitoke beaches. Tadpoles are found in standing water from September onwards, and the adults' calls consist of a series of loud, harsh croaks.

HIDDEN TREASURES

Below: New Zealand's most ancient reptile, the rare tuatara, was once found all over Great Barrier, especially in association with burrow-nesting seabirds. Despite their large size (up to 20 times larger than skinks), tuatara cannot survive with cats and rats. Their extreme longevity (up to a hundred years) means that some large old individuals may yet be surviving in remote places on the island.

Len Doel

Right: Like the other large *Cyclodina* skinks, robust skinks are now critically endangered and restricted to a few small sanctuaries. Their ground-dwelling and nocturnal nature, large size and low reproductive rate make them easy prey for rats and cats. Predator control will be needed before *Cyclodina* skinks can be re-established in Great Barrier's forests.

Len Doel

Great Barrier is a large island, and biological surveys are typically brief and cannot cover all areas. It is therefore possible that the island supports species that have not been seen for many years or are known from other islands. Within the last two decades, three lizard species never before seen on Great Barrier have been found. Current disjunct distributions of robust skink (*Cyclodina alani*), McGregor's skink (*C. macgregori*) and Whitaker's skink (*C. whitakeri*) strongly suggest that they were once widespread on the mainland and were probably on large islands such as Great Barrier. Tuatara (*Sphenodon punctatus*) are found on nearby islands and would certainly have once been on Great Barrier. A few individuals may yet be hanging on in remote (or not so remote) areas of the island.

W ith its long, much-indented coastline, Great Barrier Island provides a diversity of habitat types for coastal marine plants and animals. The island's waters are also visited by more oceanic animals than the inshore waters of the Hauraki Gulf — ranging from pelagic fish and whales to tropical reef fish, manta rays, turtles and sea-snakes. The tropical influence is shared with other offshore islands in the region — the Poor Knights and Mokohinaus — and results from periodic incursions of warmer and more saline waters from the East Auckland Current. This major current originates off the Queensland coast and flows eastward past Lord Howe and Norfolk Islands before travelling down the east coast of Northland.

The immediate nearshore environment of Great Barrier is generally shallow (less than 30 metres). Water deeper than 50 metres is found close to the shore only around the northern tip of Aotea and off the northern and eastern coasts of Rakitu Island. The water is generally very clear, particularly on the east coast with its more oceanic aspect and the absence of turbid runoff from the land. Despite this, few underwater surveys have been conducted around Great Barrier, and most published information is about the north-eastern coast.

Aerial view of the rugged, highly dissected eastern coastline of Great Barrier Island. Generally the lifeforms of these shores are similar to those on exposed eastern coasts of Northland.

Brent Baker

Great Barrier is reasonably well endowed with fresh waters, although the streams are generally small and there are no lakes. Several wetlands have survived deforestation and pastoral development of the low-lying and flatter lands. All the freshwater fishes present on Great Barrier are also present on the nearby mainland, although not all of the mainland species are present on Great Barrier.

MARINE HABITATS

THE ROCKY SHORE

Most of Great Barrier's coast is rocky, and has weathered to produce a rugged and highly dissected shoreline. The intertidal marine communities that inhabit this type of shore vary according to the degree of wave exposure. Shores on the more protected western and southern sides of the island generally share the same features as similar shores on the adjacent mainland. The upper shore is dominated by lichens, the mid shore by small acorn barnacles and oysters, the low shore by turfing seaweeds and the low-tide mark by larger seaweeds such as kelps. Shore crabs, stalked barnacles, sea anemones and carnivorous whelks abound in the numerous cracks, pools and sea caves (e.g. in the softer rocks around Tryphena). Grazing molluscs, such as limpets, chitons, topshells and cat's-eye snails, can often be found in mid intertidal areas, and the common sea urchin (kina) occurs among the low-shore seaweeds.

Limpets, chitons and topshells are among the commonest grazing animals of the rocky shore. The numerous whelks are predatory gastropods which feed on the small barnacles encrusting the rocks.

Mike Bradstock

In contrast, shores at the northern end of the island and along much of the east coast are more exposed to waves generated by ocean swells. Intertidal communities in protected bays, such as the inner parts of Rangiwhakea Bay or the western side of Rakitu Island, are similar to those on the west side. However, the shore towards the outer headlands tends to be covered more by encrusting species, such as large acorn barnacles, mussels and a greater variety of large, bushy seaweeds.

In the most exposed localities around the Needles and Aiguilles Island, inter-tidal communities are encountered that resemble those found on offshore islands to the north. This is one of the very few places in northeastern New Zealand where the large bull kelp, *Durvillaea antarctica*, is occasionally found on the lower shore, although it is common all the way up the west coast. Other unusual species on these extremely exposed shores are the mollusc *Novastoa lamellosa*, which lives in a tube attached to the rock, so that it looks more like a tubeworm, and a rare species of chiton which broods its young under the shell.

SUB-TIDAL REEFS

Generally the rocky shore around Great Barrier extends into subtidal reefs up to 50 metres deep before reaching muddy sand. The marine communities of these reefs are typical of those found on the mainland coast of north-eastern New Zealand, with the exception of a few sponge species that are more typical of warmer waters.

Four main subtidal habitats are represented around Great Barrier.

- The **shallow mixed seaweed** habitat is dominated by large brown seaweeds (mostly *Carpophyllum* species and scattered *Ecklonia radiata*), with smaller red seaweeds underneath. This habitat is restricted to the surge zone and only extends deeper than eight metres in places where there is strong wave action. At these most exposed sites, another brown seaweed, *Lessonia variegata*, is often found in large clumps.

- The second habitat, **turf flats** or **barrens**, generally lacks large seaweeds, and is dominated by turf-forming and encrusting seaweeds, particularly the greyish-pink corallines. The barren nature of this habitat is usually due to grazing by kina or sea urchins (*Evechinus chloroticus*), which reach peak densities in this zone. They sometimes feed in large aggregations, swarming over kelp plants and rapidly devouring them.

Shallow subtidal reef habitat. Sea urchins graze among turf-forming seaweeds and spotties forage the rock-shelf above.

Mike Bradstock

- The large kelp *Ecklonia radiata* dominates below the kina barrens, and forms a distinctive lush underwater forest (aptly called the **kelp forest** habitat), with a diverse assemblage of encrusting seaweeds, sponges, ascidians (sea squirts) and bryozoans occurring underneath it.

- The deepest reef habitat is the **sponge garden**, which is dominated by large sponges and other encrusting animals, and found where sunlight is insufficient to allow much seaweed to grow. This may be as shallow as 15 metres in more turbid areas and as deep as 35 metres in clear water. On much of the north-eastern coast, the kelp forest extends to well over 25 metres and the nature of the deep sponge community is consequently not well known.

A deep-water sponge community at 30 metres. Massive black sponge (*Ancorina*) is surrounded by variously coloured encrusting sponges, bryozoans and colonial ascidians. The sea urchin is *Centrostephanus rogersi*.

Mike Bradstock

While the above habitat types generally follow a predictable sequence down a depth gradient at Great Barrier, this trend is interrupted in some places by patches of other habitat types, depending on local topography of the reef, particularly in the north-east. For instance, the shallow area between Rakitu Island and the coast between Whangapoua and Harataonga has extensive areas of cobbles and pebbles, which support many and varied large bushy red and green seaweeds. Further north, the very large angular blocks of rock east of Aiguilles Island have sheer faces rising from a depth of 25 metres almost to the surface. At shallow depths these support dense beds of agar seaweed (*Pterocladia lucida*), and deeper down there are colourful jewel anemones, ascidians and hydroids.

A red rock lobster peers out from under wreckage of the *Wairarapa* (see p.27).

Roger Grace

The beautiful but sharp-pointed tropical sea urchin *Diadema palmeri*.

Len Doel

The broken reefs provide excellent habitat for crabs and crayfish. While the red rock lobster (*Jasus edwardsii*) is the most common, two other species, Spanish lobster and packhorse crayfish (*J. verreauxi*), are patchily distributed but regularly seen. The packhorse crayfish, New Zealand's largest crustacean, is restricted mainly to northern areas of the country. Up to four packhorse crayfish per 100 square metres were recorded in underwater surveys at Harataonga Bay in the early 1990s — much higher than found in similar surveys on the adjacent mainland coast. In the early 1900s they were even more plentiful — and bigger, with specimens over a metre long and more than 20 kg in weight commonly encountered.

As well as the common kina, three species of warmer-water sea urchins have been reported in shallow waters around Great Barrier — *Centrostephanus rodgersi*, *Heliocidaris tuberculata* and the long-spined, tropical *Diadema palmeri*. Paua or abalone, a group of large grazing molluscs, are also common, especially the black-foot paua (*Haliotis iris*), though it never grows as large as its southern counterparts and has become much less abundant. The other two species (*H. australis,* yellow-foot paua, and *H. virginea,* virgin paua) are smaller, rarer and more cryptic. The suite of other subtidal, reef-dwelling molluscs found on mainland shores in the region are also common on Great Barrier and include turban shells, cat's-eye snails, various topshells, limpets and several large whelks. Chitons are numerous on the undersides of boulders or loose rocks, as well as on the cobble beds at 10 to 15 metres depth west of Rakitu Island, with 10 species easily found. This gravel-and-cobble habitat also supports carpets of the bright green alga *Caulerpa flexilis*, encrusting bryozoans, ascidians and sponges, several crab species and nudibranchs (sea slugs).

More than 70 species of fish have been recorded from the subtidal reefs on the north-eastern coast, although the total is probably even greater.

Triplefins (Family Tripterygiidae), also known as cockabullies, are the most diverse fish group, with at least

seven species. These small, cryptic fishes hide in cracks or around the bases of boulders, darting out to feed on small crustaceans, snails or juvenile fish. Other common reef fish are hiwihiwi, porae, moray eels, leatherjackets, red moki and wrasses (spotties, red pigfish, Sandager's wrasse, banded wrasse). Seaweed-eating species include butterfish, marblefish, parore, silver drummer and black angelfish. This last fish, *Parma alboscapularis*, is only rarely found around the mainland, where the waters are more turbid: it is more abundant at offshore islands, in shallow waters usually in or close to kelp forest. Mature males keep territories and entice the females in to mate and lay eggs in 'nests', patches of rock up to half a metre square that they

Black angelfish (adult, left, juvenile, below) are common in shallow water around the kelp forests at Great Barrier.

Malcolm Francis

have cleared of all seaweed. The male then defends the nest vigorously until the young fish hatch.

A demoiselle guarding its nesting site among encrusting algae and small animals on a rock face.

Mike Bradstock

Another species that lays eggs in a nest and is relatively uncommon on the mainland but abundant at Great Barrier and other offshore islands is the demoiselle, *Chromis dispilus*.

Large schools of these small fish flit above the kelp and along the faces of vertical drop-offs, feeding mainly on small shrimp-like plankton. Two other common plankton-feeders are sweep and blue maomao. Another group of fish is typified by species such as snapper, tarakihi, goatfish and blue cod. These are not so closely associated with the reef itself, but do much of their feeding over adjacent sandy or shell habitats.

The northern area of Great Barrier has a distinct sub-tropical element among its reef-fish community. At least seven species are found that are typical of more tropical waters and in New Zealand found only at northern offshore islands: yellow-banded perch, grey moray, notchhead marblefish, clown toady, black-spotted goatfish, toadstool groper and crimson cleanerfish. At Great Barrier, these species are believed to be rare, perhaps because the warm East Auckland Current only occasionally brings their larvae into the island's nearshore waters. Greater numbers and a wider range of species will probably be found if global warming is a reality.

ESTUARIES

Estuarine vegetation is a major feature of only one harbour — Whangapoua. Here, mangroves (*Avicennia marina*) form an impressive forest on the intertidal sediment flats behind the protective sandspit. These trees have a largely tropical distribution, and only occur in New Zealand north of 38°S. At Whangapoua, the main forest covers approximately 70 hectares, with trees up to three metres tall along the channel edges. The mangrove flowers in late summer and the fruits take 9 to 10 months to develop. These are released as floating propagules, which soon shed their yellow outer skin to reveal the bright green, fleshy seed-leaves that will nourish the

Mangrove fruits (upper) germinate within hours of falling off the tree and rapidly find attachment in the estuary mud.
Below: Inundated by a high spring tide, the mangrove forest is a warm and sheltered habitat with abundant food - an ideal nursery habitat for young fishes.

Mike Bradstock

young mangrove plants. Usually thought of as mud-dwelling plants, in fact the mangroves of Whangapoua live in relatively clean sand, and the water is rarely turbid. Consequently, only a few pneumatophores (breathing roots) are required. Scattered patches of seagrass are present around the lower reaches of the mangrove forest. Further up the Whangapoua estuary, mangroves are replaced by salt-marsh plants which form a luxuriant meadow up to 300 metres wide in some places (see p.59).

The sediments among the salt-marshes and mangroves support mud crabs (particularly *Helice crassa*) and mud snails, with the large, air-breathing species *Amphibola crenata* being the most common. Cockles abound in the sandier sediments beyond the mangroves, and pipi occur on the inner side of the sandspit and in the channel at the mouth of the harbour. These have long been harvested for food.

Because most of the water empties out at low tide, few fish reside permanently in estuaries like Whangapoua. Small species like gobies and estuarine triplefin shelter in holes in the bottom. Visiting fish such as smelt, yellow-eyed mullet and juvenile kahawai regularly enter the estuary at high tide to feed on estuarine plankton or the nutritive deposits that accumulate on the mud surface. Snapper and flounder come in to feed on crabs, bivalves and other bottom-dwelling invertebrates. Other fish that may be found in Whangapoua are whitebait and eels, which pass through on their way to the freshwater streams that form their main habitat.

Mangroves and other estuary lifeforms also occur sporadically in the protected bays of some other harbours, although there are not the same extensive intertidal flats as at Whangapoua. For example, there are extensive mangroves at Wairahi Bay and small mangrove clumps among the shore cobbles at Tryphena and Port Fitzroy, and along the lower banks of Kaitoke Stream. Mangroves in these places often grow taller than at Whangapoua and have much straighter trunks. These very sheltered, muddy, intertidal habitats also support mud crabs, with the pebbles providing grazing surfaces for topshells and several chitons that live under boulders.

OCEAN BEACHES

Ocean beaches are a feature of the south-east coast of Great Barrier, with notable ones at Whangapoua, Awana, Kaitoke and Medlands. The clean white sand here supports many small invertebrates such as polychaete worms, amphipods and isopods. More conspicuous to the casual observer are the edible tuatua (*Paphies subtriangulata*), sand-dollars (*Arachnoides zelandica*) and paddle crabs (*Ovalipes catharus*), which all abound at and just below the lowest tidal levels. More sheltered beaches, but still with tuatuas, occur in the upper parts of some of the west coast bays and harbours such as Tryphena and Blind Bay.

Further offshore a great variety of gastropods and bivalves live in the sandy sediments, and their shells are often washed ashore on the ocean beaches after storms. Some, like the sunrise shell, *Tawera spissa*, live in extremely dense beds, but others are more scattered. Scallops (*Pecten novaezelandiae*) have become much less common in recent years. Other invertebrates common in subtidal sediments are hermit crabs and other crustaceans, brittlestars, heart urchins and polychaete worms. These worms are often gregarious, living in tubes and forming extensive mats in deeper, muddier sediments. The large tubeworm *Chaetopterus* sp. has become extremely abundant at these depths throughout the outer Hauraki Gulf since 1997, and its parchment tubes, up to 30 centimetres long, are washed ashore after storms.

All the bottom-dwelling marine invertebrates tend to be patchy in distribution, but predictable associations can often be found at certain depths and within particular sediment types. For example, five major associations, three of which are dominated by different bivalve species, have been recorded from a 20-kilometre-square area of seabed (3 to 60 metres in depth) off Rangiwhakaea Bay. Some unusual inhabitants also live in offshore sediments. Snake eels (Family Ophichthidae), for example, live in burrows in the sand or mud, and occasionally are caught on lines.

Though only the head shows, this snake eel burrowing in sandy offshore sediment may be more than two metres in length.

Roger Grace

OFFSHORE OPEN WATERS

Great Barrier's offshore waters support a rich marine fauna that is ultimately based on phytoplankton and zooplankton. Large schools of koheru, jack mackerel, pink and blue maomao and sweep feed directly on the zooplankton. So do large and solitary fish like the sunfish or the occasional manta ray, and baleen whales. Bottom-feeding species like eaglerays, stingrays, snapper, tarakihi and goatfish prey on invertebrates living in the bottom sediments.

Many fish have a varied diet and will take plankton,

Stingrays like this large specimen at Port Abercrombie can quite safely be approached by divers. They are only likely to be dangerous if molested or accidentally stepped on.

Roger Grace

STINGRAYS AND EAGLERAYS

Two types of rays are among the fish you are most likely to see at Great Barrier, even if you don't venture into the water. In the Whangapoua estuary, for instance, rays are a common sight, gliding along the edges of the main channel, their 'wingtips' at times almost out of the water, or resting still after stirring up a cloud of sand with their wings. They also swim around the island's wharves, where burrowing animals which they eat are exposed as the wash of large passenger ferries stirs up the bottom. They are common in most of Great Barrier's marine habitats, including harbours, beaches and estuaries, rocky coasts, reefs and open seabed.

The easiest way to tell them apart at a glance is by the way they swim. Stingrays move their wings in a graceful rippling motion, while eaglerays flap theirs in bird-like fashion. Stingrays grow considerably larger — to three metres long and up to 150 kg.

Contrary to popular belief they are not predators in the same league as sharks. Their mouths are small with two hard flat plates which they use to crush crabs and molluscs. Eaglerays in particular feed on Cook's turban shells, and both species prey on the paddle crabs common around the island's beaches.

As with their relatives the sharks, rays can sense disturbances in the electric field around them caused by other animals. Eaglerays sometimes school together.

small fish or bottom-dwelling invertebrates. Kahawai, for instance, can be seen around Great Barrier either individually, in small groups or as large schools, and forage from the surface to the seabed. The adults may eat planktonic crustaceans, small schooling fishes, or crabs, molluscs and worms from the seafloor. Finally, there are species that are almost completely carnivorous on larger, swimming prey such as other fish and squid. This group includes tuna, kingfish, hapuku and john dory, as well as sperm whales and sharks.

If disturbed, rays will explode out of the sand and in most cases flee at great speed, They are not aggressive, but if cornered they lash about with the serrated barb or barbs at the base of their tails, sawing and stabbing.

Rays give birth tail-first to live young in the shallow bays during summer. The wings immediately unfold ready to swim. The tail barbs of baby rays are encased in a gelatinous material at the time of birth, to protect the mother.

Eaglerays can be distinguished at a glance from stingrays (opposite) by their more kite-like shape and the greenish coloration with blue blotches. They also swim differently: an eagleray flaps its wings like a bird, but the stingray's wings ripple at the edge.

Roger Grace

The more rapid water currents around steep-sided offshore pinnacles such as the Needles, Pigeons, Broken Islands or Horn Rock attract plankton-feeding fish and large roving fish such as kingfish and kahawai. Hapuku are more likely to be found in these places, too, especially in the deepest water, and sharks such as bronze whalers and hammerheads may be encountered. Their smaller relations such as school sharks and rig are more likely to be seen in the large bays and harbours on the western side, where they come to give birth to their young (called 'pups') over the summer months.

Large whales frequently pass by Great Barrier, and the passage between Great Barrier and Little Barrier leading into Colville Channel seems to be well used. Whales were almost certainly more numerous in the early twentieth century, when the toothed sperm whale was commonly encountered along with two baleen whales, the humpback and the Bryde's. The humpback (*Megoptera novaeangliae*) is now an endangered species. It feeds in Antarctic waters over summer, but migrates north to Tonga, Samoa and Fiji to breed in winter, with the majority passing northward along New Zealand's east coast in autumn. Bryde's whale (*Balaenoptera edeni*) is mainly tropical but ranges down along the Northland coast in spring and stays around until autumn. Bryde's whales were captured in large numbers around Great Barrier in the late 1950s and early 60s and processed at Whangaparapara.

Sperm whales (*Physeter macrocephalus*) and long-finned pilot whales (*Globiocephala melaena*) often pass by, and strandings of both species have been documented.

A pod of sperm whales stranded at Okupu in 1972.

George Medland

Other common toothed whales around Great Barrier are the large orca (*Orcinus orca*), often seen in pods; the smaller bottlenosed dolphin (*Tursiops truncatus*), seen singly or in small groups; and the even smaller common dolphin (*Delphinus delphis*), almost always seen in groups, some numbering up to a thousand animals. All feed on schooling fish, although orca also eat rays. Sea snakes, manta rays and turtles visit northern New Zealand from tropical waters and are sometimes seen from boats.

FRESHWATER HABITATS

Great Barrier's streams and wetlands host more freshwater species than any other New Zealand offshore island. A recent survey recorded seven freshwater species, but did not find three other species recorded in the past.

Inanga, the most common whitebait species, occurs on Great Barrier as well as mainland New Zealand.

Bob McDowall

The fish fauna that inhabits Great Barrier's freshwater streams and wetlands has three key characteristics. First, all species spend some time in the sea when newly hatched, and return to fresh water while still small. Second, several species present in North Island fresh waters close by, such as Coromandel and the Auckland area, have so far not been found on Great Barrier. Third, exotic freshwater fishes do not appear to be present on Great Barrier.

Few juvenile fish of any species appear to be present in Great Barrier's fresh waters. This may be due to the distance between Great Barrier and mainland New Zealand, and the lack of big river systems discharging large volumes of fresh water into the sea which stimulate the fish to migrate upstream.

Some species, such as eels, banded and giant kokopu, koaro and possibly the giant bully, are long-lived, which means that populations of these species will remain over long periods even though few new fish may join them each year. For short-lived species like inanga and bluegill bully, however, populations may fluctuate widely, and sometimes these species may be absent from island streams until further recruitment takes place.

The longfin eel (*Anguilla dieffenbachii*), New Zealand's most widespread native fish, is found in streams throughout the island. It favours the cover of boulders, overhanging banks and deeper pools. Although nocturnal, it is occasionally seen out foraging by day. The shortfin eel (*A. australis*) is also nocturnal, and is most common in wetlands and estuaries.

Great Barrier's freshwater galaxiids contribute to whitebait fisheries on the mainland, but are nowhere abundant enough on Great Barrier to serve the same purpose. Inanga (*Galaxias maculatus*) is the principal whitebait species, and is found on Great Barrier mainly in small, loose shoals, at low elevations and in gently flowing pools and runs. Banded kokopu (*G. fasciatus*), a somewhat rarer species in the mainland whitebait fishery, is widely distributed throughout the island, especially where there is

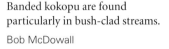

Banded kokopu are found particularly in bush-clad streams.

Bob McDowall

thick bush cover over streams. This fish is mostly nocturnal.

A third whitebait species is the giant kokopu, *G. argenteus*, which can reach 40 centimetres in length. Little is known about its presence on Great Barrier, although there are historical and recent anecdotal records to suggest it does occur. When found, it will likely be in overgrown lowland streams, especially where there are deep pools with plenty of cover. It is also nocturnal but is sometimes seen by day if undisturbed. Little also is known about the koaro (*G. brevipinnis*), which will be found mostly at higher elevations, more usually in larger, swift, bouldery waters, where it occupies the spaces in the riffles. It emerges to feed at night.

Four species of bully are known from Great Barrier. The redfin (*Gobiomorphus huttoni*), a handsome fish living in rocky streams, is widely present on the island at low to

Redfin bullies are widespread in Great Barrier streams.

Bob McDowall

mid elevations, but tends to be secretive, emerging into pools to feed at night. It is likely that populations closer to the coastline consist mostly of small juveniles that have recently moved upstream from the sea. The giant bully, *G. gobioides*, is New Zealand's largest native bully, reaching as much as 20 centimetres long. It is little known, owing to its secretive habits. The giant bully lives among boulders and under overhung banks and woody debris in lowland streams, and may feed at night out in pools.

The common bully, *G. cotidianus,* has rarely been found in Great Barrier streams, perhaps because it is more open-living than the other species. On the mainland it is found around lake shores and in estuaries. Although the presence of the bluegill bully (*G. hubbsi*) on Great Barrier is known from anecdotal records, it was only recently that this species was definitely recorded for the first time. The rarity of earlier records is not surprising, as this fish is very small (to 7 centimetres in length), slender and favours swiftly flowing riffles, making it difficult to detect. Great Barrier is the first island from which the bluegill has been recorded.

Two fishes that mostly frequent marine and estuarine waters have also been recorded in Great Barrier's freshwater areas: the cockabully (*Grahamina nigripenne*) and the dart goby (*Parioglossus marginalis*). The cockabully is a common estuarine triplefin, and is probably widely present in habitats close to the upper limits of tidal influence.

The dart goby was recently discovered on Great Barrier in the Kaitoke wetland. It was the first record of this fish anywhere in New Zealand, but soon after it was also found in streams near North Cape. A tiny fish, only up to about 4 centimetres long, the dart goby has a dark stripe running along each side of its body and across the tail to its hind margin. It is primarily a marine fish, and it seems that in the Kaitoke wetland it lives mostly in a 'wedge' of salt water that penetrates a long distance upstream, forming a saline layer beneath the fresh water.

The giant bully grows to 20 cm long but is seldom seen owing to its secretive habits.

Bob McDowall

Great Barrier's streams also have freshwater mussels. These shellfish bury themselves in the silt, where they feed by siphoning in stream water and then extracting out algae and other tiny organisms.

USE OF AQUATIC RESOURCES

The reefs and waters around Great Barrier Island have long been the target of commercial and recreational fishing. The once prolific populations of seabirds that roosted and bred along the east coast are thought to have declined dramatically in the 1950s as a result of very large catches by foreign and local vessels of the fish and squid on which the birds feed. Restrictions were gradually introduced after the 1950s, and the quota management system of 1986 has put limits on the catches of many species.

A 1993 survey noted that people from Auckland, Leigh and the Coromandel ports, as well as those based at Great Barrier, regularly fished the island's north-eastern coast for species such as snapper, rock lobster, hapuku, bass, tarakihi, trevally, red moki, john dory, porae, kahawai and school shark. The commercial methods still used are mainly trawling, Danish seining, long-lining and rock lobster

A snapper on a commercial long-line. Snapper is the most valuable commercial fish in the Hauraki Gulf but catches have become restricted by the quota management system.

Mike Bradstock

potting. However, commercial fishing around the island appears to have declined since 1993. Scallop fishing, too, appears to be in decline.

One commercial venture that is apparently doing well is mussel farming, with nine farms in Port Fitzroy and Katherine Bay. Strong currents bring a good supply of food (phytoplankton) to the suspended ropes on which green-lipped mussels are grown.

Great Barrier used to be viewed as a paradise for recreational fishing. In the early 1960s, line, net and spear-fishing yielded good catches of large snapper, kingfish, crayfish, porae, red moki and other species. Since that time, fish stocks around the island appear to have declined dramatically, though not as much as the mainland stocks.

Much of the freshwater habitats and fauna on Aotea is already protected within DOC reserves, but at present there is no such protection for the marine environment. In 1994, DOC lodged a detailed proposal for a marine reserve in the island's northeastern waters. It covered 14 kilometres of coast between Waikaro Point and Whakatautuna Point and extended seaward to surround Rakitu Island. The site was chosen because of its wide range of marine habitats within a relatively small area (40 square kilometers). While the proposal stalled (despite substantial public support), the reasoning behind it remains valid.

In January 2001 DOC announced its intention to proceed with investigations for a marine reserve on the northeast coast of Great Barrier. With research already having been carried out for the previous proposal, and further surveys to establish other potential sites, it is to be hoped that the marine reserves that result will provide a lasting testament to the rich and spectacular marine life of Great Barrier.

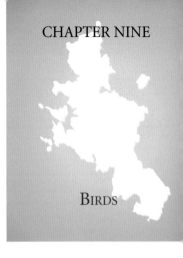

CHAPTER NINE

BIRDS

S ome of the predatory animals introduced to New Zealand in the nineteenth century by Europeans have never become established on Great Barrier. This is why birds which are now rare or absent on the mainland are still present on the island — for example, black petrel, brown teal and kaka. However, to appreciate fully the composition of the bird life we see on Great Barrier today, and more particularly the potential for restoring missing species, we need to understand what the island was like in prehistoric times.

About 20,000 years ago, when Great Barrier was part of northern New Zealand, it presumably shared most of its fauna, which was dominated by flightless birds, reptiles and large invertebrates. The land was probably almost completely forested apart from wetlands, rocky outcrops and sea cliffs. Grasslands and herbfields would have been confined to wetland margins and the youngest dunes.

At least six of the 11 known species of moa probably occurred there, from the 30 kg bush moa *Anomalopteryx* to the 170 kg giant moa *Dinornis*. Moa were mainly herbivores, browsing on the twigs, shoots, leaves and fruits of a wide range of shrubs and trees. The other main ground herbivore in this environment would have been takahe, mainly in wetlands, coastal grasslands and herbfields.

In the forest many other birds, including species now extinct, would have been present. Ground-level species would have included brown and little spotted kiwi, adzebill, weka, several small rails, snipe and probably two species of flightless wrens. In the lower levels of the forest vegetation were bush wren, robin, saddleback, huia and piopio. Higher up in the trees, kaka, red- and yellow-crowned kakariki (parakeets), kereru (native pigeon), kingfisher, long-tailed and shining cuckoos, rifleman, tomtit, whitehead, fantail, grey warbler, tui, bellbird, stitchbird and kokako were probably also common. In addition to kiwi, nocturnal forest species probably included kakapo, laughing owl, morepork and owlet-nightjar.

The North Island saddleback probably disappeared quickly once ship rats became established on Great Barrier. If predatory mammals can be removed, saddlebacks could be re-introduced to both Great Barrier and Rakitu Islands.

Len Doel

Recent releases to islands such as Tiritiri Matangi show that takahe can survive and breed on northern islands free of predators.

Len Doel

The wetlands would have hosted takahe and fernbird, as well as pukeko, brown teal, Finch's duck, grey duck, grey teal, shoveler, musk duck, flightless goose, bittern and crakes. Open areas along wetland and forest margins would have harboured New Zealand quail.

These prehistoric habitats did have some predators, including morepork, laughing owl, the giant eagle, goshawk, harrier and falcon. On the ground, along with the weka, another important predator would have been the adzebill, a flightless species like a giant heavy-billed weka. In open areas and along the coast, the extinct crow might have been a predator of shore bird nests as well as a scavenger of carrion.

Seabirds, especially burrowing petrels, would have been abundant. Many species which today survive on Great Barrier only in small numbers, or breed only on remote islands free of predators, would have bred on the mainland. These tubenose birds would probably have included black, Cook's, grey-faced and mottled petrels, flesh-footed, sooty, little and fluttering shearwaters, fairy prions and diving petrels.

Along the coast, a roughly similar range of shore birds as seen today would have been present, with the addition of shore plover and the extinct pelican. Some, such as New Zealand dotterel, might have been more abundant than now.

When the sea level rose after the last glaciation and Great Barrier became separated from the mainland, the area of land shrank. Some species, such as large moa, which probably required large areas of habitat to maintain viable populations, may have declined or become locally extinct.

Humans and their animals added to the eventual extinction or depletion of many species. In general, the early Maori first targeted the large diurnal 'meaty' species (for example, moa) and birds that were easy to catch. Possible evidence of moa hunting on Great Barrier comes from a midden at Harataonga, where bones of the stout-legged moa, *Euryapteryx geranoides*, have been found. Other species vulnerable to human predation were the colonial nesting shorebirds, pelicans and petrels, whose eggs and young could be easily gathered.

The dog (kuri) and Pacific rat (kiore) brought by early Polynesians were probably responsible for a wave of early extinctions of birds, reptiles and invertebrates. Vulnerable ground birds such as snipe, small rails, owlet-nightjar and flightless wrens were probably exterminated by kiore early in the Polynesian period. Kiore might also have preyed on the young of some of the smaller moa and competed with them for food. Kuri could have preyed on many ground-inhabiting birds near settlements, much as dogs today prey on kiwi, penguins, weka and brown teal. By the time the first Europeans arrived, it appears that all 11 species of moa were extinct, along with the pelican, swan, goose, at least four species of duck, three species of birds of prey, five species of rail, adzebill, owlet-nightjar, three species of wren and the crow.

Fortunately the Norway rat, which on the mainland probably preyed on native quail, saddleback, huia and piopio, never became established on Great Barrier. Those animals that did include cats, mice, ship rats, rabbits, goats, pigs, fallow deer, dogs and domestic livestock.

An account of the birds of Great Barrier by Frederick Wollaston Hutton in 1868 (see panel, p.150) suggests that cats and ship rats were either still absent or rare, because he recorded a number of species that are known to be very vulnerable to these predators, including shore plover, red-crowned kakariki, stitchbird and saddleback. These last three, which nest and roost in tree holes, are particularly vulnerable to the ship rat, which climbs trees and takes eggs, young and adult birds.

Great Barrier remains one of the largest areas in New Zealand where mustelids (weasels, stoat and ferrets) have not become established. This is very significant for preserving existing birds and for future ecological restoration. On the mainland, mustelids have accelerated the decline of many native birds (for example, kiwi, various petrels, brown teal, kakapo and kaka), which had already been greatly diminished by European rats and feral cats. The continued existence of black petrel, brown teal, banded rail and kaka on Great Barrier today is probably mainly due to the lack of mustelids.

HUTTON'S LIST

Frederick Wollaston Hutton (1836–1905) was a university professor and museum curator who made a major contribution to the field of biology in New Zealand during the late nineteenth century.

His account of the birds present on Great Barrier in the mid-nineteenth century is both fascinating and sad. It was produced at a time when the Maori and their animals had probably already had all the effect they ever would, but before the full effects of European colonisation had been felt. Hutton recorded a number of species now rare or extinct on Great Barrier, such as shore plover, stitchbird, saddleback, falcon, red- and yellow-crowned kakariki, long-tailed cuckoo, bellbird, rifleman, whitehead, robin, tomtit and kokako.

He also mentioned the now-extinct New Zealand quail as occurring on Flat Island, but noted that it had disappeared from there several years before his visit. He recorded a number of tubenoses, of which little shearwater, black, Cook's and diving petrels were described as being very common.

The grey-faced petrel is not on Hutton's list. However, given that he visited during summer, this winter breeder could have been overlooked. Nor did he record kiwi, rails or pukeko.

Hutton's Maori informants had no knowledge of kiwi on the island, which seems odd as there was plenty of suitable habitat, as there still is today. Perhaps the kiwi was a victim of over-hunting by Maori, aided by dogs. Less likely, perhaps it never occurred on Great Barrier. It is curious also that Hutton did not record pukeko or rails, especially given the presence of banded rail today.

Ducks were also scarce, with only the grey duck being recorded. Brown teal must have been present, but were probably overlooked. Teal may have suffered from over-hunting by Maori and European settlers and predation by their dogs, and so been in very low numbers when Hutton visted. The conspicuous population of teal there today may be a recent phenomenon.

PRESENT BIRDLIFE

SEABIRDS

The seas and islands inside the Poor Knights and Great Barrier have one of the world's highest diversities of petrels and shearwaters, with 13 breeding species. At least five of these still breed on Great Barrier and surrounding islets, and most of them can be seen at sea around the island. During winter, some of the local seabirds migrate to the northern and eastern Pacific, and are replaced by migrants from southern waters, such as wandering albatross, Salvin's, black-browed and yellow-nosed mollymawks, giant petrel and cape pigeon.

The most significant species resident on Great Barrier is the black petrel, which formerly bred on many inland ranges of the mainland, but is now known to breed only on Great and Little Barrier Islands. The total population is believed to be 3-4,000 birds, including about 900 breeding pairs. Great Barrier is now the stronghold for this species, with 800 pairs breeding on Mt Hobson (Hirakimata) and

During summer, black petrels can be seen at sea between the Northland coast and the Barrier Islands. When flying they can be distinguished from other local large, dark petrels by their ivory-coloured bills and black feet projecting beyond the centre of the tail.

Craig Potton

on nearby peaks and ridges above 300 metres. The other 100 pairs breed on the high summit ridges of Little Barrier. Feral cats nearly exterminated the Little Barrier colony, which is partly why cats were eradicated on this island in the late 1970s. Black petrels are large enough to defend their nests from ship rats, and their eggs are too large for rats to break open. However, unguarded young can be at risk from rats and feral cats. Black petrels are vulnerable to dogs, which are now banned from the Mt Hobson area.

Recent studies of the Great Barrier colony have shown that productivity is high. This made it possible to conduct experimental transfers between 1986 and 1990 of about 250 young black petrels to Little Barrier to boost numbers in the smaller, now predator-free colony. Black petrels breed during the summer, with the first breeders returning to their burrows from the tropical eastern Pacific from mid-October onwards. Only one egg is laid, and the young depart between April and July. Although there is some risk from predators at their Great Barrier breeding sites, the major threat to black petrels now is probably accidental capture in pelagic long-line fisheries.

The small grey-and-white Cook's petrel used to breed on Great Barrier in large numbers. However, they have been exterminated from the mainland and greatly diminished on Great Barrier by introduced predators. They now breed only

The blue penguin was formerly a very common breeding bird on the islands of the Hauraki Gulf and the surrounding mainland, but at many of these places, including Great Barrier, it is threatened by dogs and other predators.

Len Doel

on Great and Little Barrier Islands, and Codfish Island off Stewart Island. Little Barrier has by far the most, with some 50,000 pairs. Possibly fewer than 20 pairs survive on Great Barrier, and they are threatened by rats and feral cats. On Great Barrier, Cook's petrels used to be killed by cats along the track up the Kaiarara Valley, but these days, because so few now breed on the island, very little sign is seen of them. On misty summer evenings, however, their harsh *kek-kek-kek* calls can still be heard over Port Fitzroy as they fly inland, evidence that a few pairs still attempt to breed there.

The grey-faced petrel is the common winter-breeding petrel on many islands in the Hauraki Gulf.

Len Doel

Probably the most widespread petrel around Great Barrier is the grey-faced, which still breeds during the winter on many offshore stacks and on a few headlands on the main island. This large, dark petrel is especially active around its colonies from March onwards. It is the traditional muttonbird of northern Maori, who harvest the young in November. These petrels can be seen offshore just before dusk, when they gather before heading to their breeding colonies.

Some of the small islets west of Port Fitzroy still have colonies of smaller petrels and shearwaters. A few pairs of fluttering shearwaters breed on Saddle Island just off Port Fitzroy, and a rat-free stack north of the Broken Islands has colonies of fluttering shearwaters and diving petrels.

The blue penguin breeds along the rocky coasts of Great

Barrier. The lack of mustelids probably benefits this species. However, blue penguins are very vulnerable to dogs, and local residents report that penguins are not as common as they used to be.

At Mahuki Island, at the southern end of the Broken Islands group, there is a large colony of about 2,500 pairs of gannets. This is a long-established colony, which is known to have been in existence in the 1860s and can easily be seen from the sea to the southwest of Mahuki. Like other gannet colonies around New Zealand, it is growing. It is estimated there were only 325 pairs in 1946. This may merely be a return to pre-human population numbers, because gannets are now protected. Gannets are spectacular to observe at sea, especially when diving en masse into shoals of fish.

Australasian gannets return to their breeding colonies in June and the young depart in February. The young then spend up to seven years in Australian waters before returning to New Zealand to breed.

Len Doel

COASTAL AND SHORE BIRDS

The range of coastal and shore birds on Great Barrier is similar to other parts of northern New Zealand. These species include pied, black, little and little black shags, red-billed and black-backed gulls, white-fronted and Caspian terns, reef and white-faced herons, variable and South Island pied oystercatchers, New Zealand and banded dotterels, wrybill, pied stilt and several species of migrant Arctic waders, including bar-tailed godwit and golden plover.

Clockwise from left:

The pied shag is the common large black and white shag around the northern New Zealand coastline.

Bar-tailed godwits on Great Barrier feed mainly in the Whangapoua estuary.

White-faced herons are widespread on Great Barrier, both around the coast and on open country inland.

Variable oystercatchers occur most commonly on Great Barrier along the east coast beaches, especially at the Whangapoua estuary and Kaitoke.

Len Doel

155

The white-fronted tern or kahawai bird is common in the Hauraki Gulf and around Great Barrier.

Len Doel

Below: The wrybill is an occasional visitor to tidal estuaries on Great Barrier.

Below left: Pied stilts occur on intertidal flats and on damp pasture inland.

Below right: Only about 1400 New Zealand dotterels exist, and they are vulnerable at their nests to predatory mammals and disturbance by people and their dogs.

Len Doel

The lack of predators makes Great Barrier an important habitat for the threatened New Zealand dotterel, with about 14 pairs along the ocean beaches of the east coast. These dotterels are still very vulnerable to predation by feral cats and disturbance by people and their dogs.

WETLAND BIRDS

Great Barrier is well known as the major remaining home of the endangered brown teal. The national population was estimated at about 2,300 in 1993, with about 1,500 of them on Great Barrier. Recent work by DOC, however, suggests that the Great Barrier population has declined, probably to 700–900 birds. On the mainland, small populations of brown teal persist in Northland and Fiordland, but without management these populations will continue to decline because of predation by introduced mammals.

The brown teal used to be abundant in many mainland wetlands, and was an easy target for shooters and introduced predators. The formerly strong Great Barrier population has declined sharply in recent years, and urgent conservation management is needed.

Dave Barker, Tim Lovegrove

On Great Barrier, teal are mainly concentrated at several sites on the eastern side of the island, where there are extensive wetlands and slow-moving coastal streams with good cover along the banks. Some also occur in the sheltered harbours along the western side of the island, where they may be seen bobbing about among moored boats or feeding on the sandy intertidal flats. At several coastal streams on the eastern side of the island — for example, Awana, Okiwi, Whangapoua and Mabey's Farm — teal form post-breeding flocks in summer. During the rest of the year they are most numerous around streams and wetlands with good cover, close to open areas of grazing land where they can feed at night on pasture invertebrates (e.g. grubs and worms.)

Okiwi Station, on the eastern side of the island, is one of the teal strongholds on Great Barrier. This important site was purchased by DOC for species conservation, in

Banded rails are scarce and elusive on the mainland, but they are widespread and quite common on Great Barrier.

Tim Lovegrove

particular brown teal management. Recent experimental manipulation of pastureland and wetlands at Okiwi, to determine the best habitat for brown teal, suggests that controlled grazing of wetlands by cattle creates the mixture of feeding, refuge and nesting habitats favoured by teal. Survival of brown teal on Great Barrier will depend on appropriate habitat management and protection, especially from predators.

Other wetland species on Great Barrier include harrier, mallard, grey and paradise ducks, pukeko, banded rail, spotless crake, kingfisher, fernbird and, rarely, bittern. The swamps at Kaitoke and Whangapoua are important sites for spotless crake and fernbird, while banded rails are widespread all over the island in wetlands, salt marshes, rough pasture and even gardens. Great Barrier may have one of the largest populations of banded rails in New Zealand. The Great Barrier fernbird population is probably the most significant in the Auckland region. Another wetland species, which may be present but is easily overlooked, is the secretive marsh crake. In the north this species prefers marshy areas at the interface of fresh water and salt water.

Fernbirds favour low, dense vegetation in both wetland and upland habitats. Their sharp clicking calls can be heard throughout the year, but especially in early spring.

Len Doel

OPEN-COUNTRY BIRDS

Rough hilly pastureland is good habitat for the New Zealand pipit, which is now rare in Auckland and Northland except on the coastal sand country. Other open-country birds include harrier, pukeko, spur-winged plover, kingfisher, welcome swallow and the introduced brown quail, skylark, dunnock, song thrush, blackbird, greenfinch, goldfinch, redpoll, chaffinch, yellowhammer, house sparrow, starling, myna and magpie.

New Zealand pipits are often seen on beaches and along dusty roadsides, where they run with a characteristic bobbing gait.

Len Doel

BUSH BIRDS

The range of bush birds is very similar to that of the larger forested areas of Auckland and Northland. A notable exception is the kaka, which is conspicuous and reasonably common. Although detailed work on kaka has not been done on Great Barrier, it again appears that the absence of predators, particularly stoats and possibly also Norway rats, enables this species to breed successfully. Like other parrots, the kaka is a hole-nesting species, and may nest in very vulnerable places in hollow trees at ground level as well as higher up. Also, young kaka are practically flightless for several days after they leave the nest, although they can climb quite well. At this stage on Great Barrier they are vulnerable to feral cats and dogs.

The local population possibly also benefits from being close to Little Barrier, where kaka are abundant. Studies

The North Island kaka is practically extinct as a breeding bird on the Auckland and Northland mainland, but strong populations survive on the Barrier and Hen and Chicken Islands.

Len Doel

The tui, morepork and fantail are all widespread on Great Barrier.

Tim Lovegrove, Len Doel

of kaka banded on Little Barrier show that these strong-flying birds are very mobile, with some ranging as far afield as Gisborne.

Other common bush birds include native pigeon, morepork, kingfisher, fantail, grey warbler and tui, and the introduced dunnock, chaffinch, blackbird, song thrush and myna. Recently, red-crowned kakariki, pied tit and bellbird have been recorded around Mt Hobson, but they are very scarce. There are also reports of red-crowned kakariki at Okiwi and bellbirds at Whangaparapara.

Until about 20 years ago, Great Barrier had the only island population of kokako, in coastal forest near Rangiwhakaea Bay at the northern end of the island. About 12 birds were found during a survey in 1984. Soon after, the population collapsed. It probably consisted mainly of old birds which were failing to nest successfully because of rat

predation and habitat deterioration caused by goat browsing. By 1993 only two remained, and these were transferred to Little Barrier. A few kokako may still persist, but unless they can be located and managed, the species is functionally extinct on Great Barrier.

Today Great Barrier's forests are devoid of many birds and the dawn chorus is not what it was. Rakitu is notable for its population of North Island weka, which were introduced from Gisborne in 1951. About 100–130 weka were present on Rakitu during a survey in 1992. Rakitu is also of note in that, apart from Little Barrier, it was the last place north of the Volcanic Plateau to have a population of whiteheads. These apparently persisted at least until the late 1950s, but died out soon after. Bellbirds also persisted on Rakitu, at least until the 1980s, but they were not found on visits during the early 1990s. These local extinctions were probably the result of deteriorating habitat caused by stock grazing, and nest predation by ship rats.

RESTORATION OF BIRDLIFE

On an island the entry of predators can be more easily controlled than on the mainland, and there are now ways of removing pests already present, even from large areas. Furthermore, Great Barrier has substantial tracts of excellent habitat, including offshore islets, ocean beaches, estuaries, wetlands, shrublands and forests; some of these areas already have populations of threatened species.

Rakitu has considerable restoration potential in the short term. Ship rats could be eradicated from this 350-hectare island. If the bush was then fenced to exclude livestock, little spotted kiwi, red-crowned kakariki, robin, whitehead and saddleback could be re-introduced. Petrels would probably gradually return unassisted, although transferring young from elsewhere could speed up this process. Obviously there would also be scope for re-introducing invertebrates and reptiles. The grazed areas could be gradually retired and returned to forest.

Some of the inshore islands around Great Barrier are very suitable for restoration, and some are small enough to be a practical proposition for local groups. Of these, Saddle Island, off Port Fitzroy, has considerable potential for petrels and reptiles. It already has at least two species of breeding petrels, and lies near a rat-free stack where diving petrels and fluttering shearwaters breed. The only problem on Saddle is the ship rat. A brief annual poisoning programme might be sufficient to keep this valuable island rat-free.

In the longer term, two main restoration options could be followed on the main island. The first is to eradicate pests from the whole 27,800 hectares. The second is to set up a substantial 'mainland island' of around 3,000 hectares, perhaps in the central part of the island with Mt Hobson at the core, and then to remove pests from that area. Having a mainland island centred round Mt Hobson would probably benefit the greatest number of species, although it could be argued that the northern end of the island, being a peninsula, might be easier to keep pest-free. Either of these mainland island options could then be expanded until the whole island became pest-free. This process would, of course, be enhanced with additional private initiatives (of which some already exist) to establish mainland islands.

Restored habitats would enable the reintroduction of many of the species seen by Hutton in the 1860s. For instance, the estuaries and open coasts could be important habitat for shore plover. Attempts could also be made to establish the endangered black stilt in estuarine habitats and wetlands in open country. This proposal would present a challenge for conservation managers, as the remaining 70 wild black stilts are now river-bed breeders, although they probably formerly bred in a wider range of habitats.

Many other forest birds could eventually be re-introduced, such as little spotted and brown kiwi, snipe, kakapo, red- and yellow-crowned kakariki, rifleman, whitehead, robin, tomtit, stitchbird, saddleback and kokako. Some, such as kakapo, are very long-term options, and would not be released until productive populations had been established elsewhere.

However, if we are to take the future protection of New Zealand's fauna seriously, large populations of some of these species should be re-established. On the mainland, attempts to establish big mainland islands are currently compromised by the difficulty of controlling mustelids, especially stoats. Unless effective ways can be found to remove them from the mainland, large ecologically restored islands such as Great Barrier may be the only feasible option for the long-term conservation of some native birds.

Little Barrier Island now supports the only large viable population of stitchbirds, but Great Barrier could be a suitable release site for this species in the future.

Tim Lovegrove

CHAPTER TEN

MANAGING THE
RESOURCE

Great Barrier Island is a key area for New Zealand's conservation work. Nearly two-thirds (approximately 19,000 hectares) of the island is public conservation land, and the main responsibility for managing its natural and historical heritage lies with the Department of Conservation (DOC). The island's conservation lands constitute the largest area managed by the department's Auckland conservancy and fall within the newly created Hauraki Gulf Marine Park. Another tenth of the island is administered by the Auckland City Council (ACC). The Auckland Regional Council (ARC) is involved with conservation activities such as animal and weed control. All three agencies have responsibilities for coastal management under the New Zealand Coastal Policy.

DOC, ACC and Ngati Rehua (Great Barrier's tangata whenua) are all involved with resource management on Great Barrier. Ngati Rehua manage significant areas of Maori land in the north, and have an interest over the whole island, particularly in regard to resources and places with cultural and traditional significance. Many island residents (who number around 1,100) also take an active interest in conservation.

A wide range of conservation activities are carried out on Great Barrier:

- *Safeguarding biological diversity*: This diversity has declined drastically over the last few hundred years as a result of large-scale clearance of forest cover and the introduction of predators, herbivores and new diseases. For example, 10 species of birds and one lizard species have disappeared from the island this century, and 12 bird species and two lizards are currently listed nationally or internationally as requiring urgent conservation action.
- *Controlling pests and weeds:* Border control is helped by the island's wide natural water barrier. It also relies on the co-operation of visitors and residents, who are alerted to the dangers of unwanted plants and animals,

particularly possums, stoats and ferrets, and asked to advise DOC of sightings of these pests. DOC, the ACC and ARC co-ordinate pest-control work on Great Barrier. This often expensive and time-consuming work targets introduced animals such as goats, feral cats and rats, and plants like pampas grass and oxygen weed. Cats and dogs are serious threats to wildlife, particularly birds and reptiles. Domestic cats should be neutered, well fed and kept inside at night. DOC traps feral cats to alleviate predator pressure around targeted sites containing threatened species. Licensed dogs are allowed on the island, but are not permitted on conservation lands or in DOC campgrounds; penalties are imposed under Auckland City bylaws. Preferably visitors should leave their pets at home.

Island residents and visitors are asked not to bring plants to Great Barrier. Even native species brought from the mainland can interfere with the integrity of Great Barrier's ecosystems.

DOC campground at Akapoua Bay, Port Fitzroy.

DOC

- *Preventing fires:* Extremely large areas of regenerating manuka and kanuka scrub on the island, and long dry summers with occasional periods of drought, make fire a major threat. DOC staff are responsible for fire control on conservation lands and a one-kilometre wide surrounding buffer zone, while local residents in various parts of the island form volunteer fire forces equipped and administered by the ACC. The two fire forces co-operate at fires and exercises, although the focus of each is different. Both DOC and the ACC advise visitors and locals of fire risk and other related hazards. Intoxicated people being careless with fire or firing off flares have been responsible for major fires in recent years. Flares should only be used in emergencies, and fires are banned at all times without a permit. Campers need to bring a gas burner for cooking.

- *Protecting significant species and sites on private land:* Many of Great Barrier's threatened plants, rare fauna and important historical sites are found on private property, and DOC works alongside individual landowners, iwi, agencies such as the Historic Places Trust, and the community to protect these resources. For example, locals are being asked to report sightings of the threatened chevron skink, the main population of which occurs on private property around Tryphena. This animal is the subject of a special DOC recovery plan.

Great Barrier also has a number of significant habitats that are still unprotected and at risk from potential subdivision or development. A number of Great Barrier landowners have protected areas of forest or wetlands on their properties, either as private projects or through covenant schemes such as those operating under the Queen Elizabeth II Trust.

- *Protecting marine resources:* None of Great Barrier's marine environments is at present protected, although a marine reserve on the north-eastern coastline is under consideration. Such a reserve would be managed by DOC with the help of local wardens, and would give full legal protection to all marine life within its boundaries. DOC also advocates for the conservation of marine species and habitats through the regional coastal plan and Marine Pollution Act and has some input into fisheries management.

Whangapoua Beach and the estuary entrance, viewed from Whiritoa Pa: an ideal marine reserve site.

Dave Barker

All marine mammals in Great Barrier's coastal waters are protected, and research is one of DOC's contributions to national and international efforts to safeguard these species. DOC is at present monitoring population changes in the Bryde's whale, the only baleen whale to regularly inhabit Great Barrier's inshore waters. DOC, assisted by Project Jonah, also mounts whale-stranding rescues or deals with carcass removals. Strandings of dolphins or whales (often large pods of pilot whales) are not uncommon in Great Barrier Island's shallow harbours.

- *Looking after historical heritage:* Many archaeological and other historical sites are located on conservation lands. DOC, in association with iwi and the Historic Places Trust, manages many of these, and researches and interprets their history. A recording scheme, established by the New Zealand Archaeological Association and managed by DOC, has resulted in an extensive index of archaeological sites.

The island has two historic reserves, Onepoto and Tapuwai Point, both of which mark graves from the *SS Wairarapa* shipwreck of 1894. Other impressive archaeological and historic sites on conservation land include wahi tapu, pa sites and relics associated with European history (see Chapter 2).

- *Undertaking surveys and monitoring programmes:* Scientific research and ongoing monitoring of species and their habitats back up DOC's management activities. Current or recent research programmes investigate chevron skink habitat preferences and response to predator control; black petrel population trends and causes of mortality; brown teal and its habitat; and search for giant stag beetles.
- *Providing visitor information and facilities:* Visitors are welcome on all public conservation lands on Great Barrier, and there is no charge for entry. Visitor facilities provided by DOC include an extensive network of walking routes and tracks, a tramping hut, picnic areas, campsites and a visitor centre at Akapoua Bay. DOC supplies maps and information on conservation areas,

Stairways like this along the Mt Hobson track make for easy access while minimising visitor impact.

Craig Potton

and interprets their natural and historic values through displays, signs and publications. The department also manages commercial concessions and hunting permits on public conservation lands.

- *Conservation advocacy:* DOC acts as an advocate for the conservation of natural and historic values and provides assistance, as appropriate, to other agencies to safeguard natural and historic values through regional and district planning and the Resource Management Act. At a community level, DOC initiates education programmes in the local schools, encourages and supports community conservation initiatives, urges island visitors to prevent fires and pest invasion, and runs volunteer programmes.

PUBLIC CONSERVATION LANDS

DOC manages 49 public conservation blocks and reserves on Great Barrier. The main ones are described here.

THE NORTH—TE PAPARAHI

Most of the Great Barrier's northern end is covered by Te Paparahi Forest, about 80 percent of which is protected within the Te Paparahi Stewardship Area. The forest is a mixture of kanuka and manuka, broadleaf species and coastal pohutukawa, and contains the largest stand of pohutukawa/taraire in New Zealand. It also hosts 10 threatened plant species, an endemic daisy, black petrels, brown teal, kaka, Hochstetter's frog, native fish and 11 species of lizard, including the chevron, striped and marble skinks (see Chapter 7). This area was once a habitat for the island's own subspecies of kokako.

Goats have been removed, but pigs, rats, feral cats and roaming stock are still a threat. The reserve shares an extensive boundary with Maori land, and DOC and Ngati Rehua work together as much as possible to achieve conservation goals. Research is being carried out to determine Te Paparahi's suitability as a 'mainland island' (see p.174).

Te Paparahi is managed as a remote wilderness area.

Mistletoe growing on manuka. This unusual native plant is threatened by introduced herbivores.

Len Doel

Part of the remote and rugged Te Paparahi Forest viewed from the air.

Brent Baker

Visitor facilities are limited to a few rough tracks, and anyone venturing into this area needs bush skills. Hunters require a permit. Camping and fires are not allowed.

THE CENTRE — GREAT BARRIER FOREST AND HIRAKIMATA (MT HOBSON) RANGE

This large contiguous area is made up of several conservation reserves: the Great Barrier Forest Conservation Area, the Great Barrier Forest Stewardship Area, the Wairahi Forest Sanctuary, and the Hirakimata-Kaitoke Swamp Ecological Area. It includes the flanks and peaks of much of the island's rugged central spine, and the island's highest peak, Mt Hobson (Hirakimata). Here are the last sizeable stands of kauri on Great Barrier, as well as extensive regenerating kauri, kanuka and manuka forest, shrublands and wetlands. A unique kauri/silver pine/mangeao community grows on Mt Hobson, along with several rare plants. Mt Hobson and other high points are the principal nesting sites for black petrel in New Zealand. Many of the island's lizards and 50 species of threatened plants are also found in Great Barrier Forest. Ground-nesting birds like the petrel are extremely vulnerable to attack and disturbance by dogs, and visitors to the Hirakimata area are especially urged to heed the 'no dogs' signs.

Great Barrier Forest was at the heart of the kauri logging industry on the island, and kauri dams, bush tramways and remnants of old mill sites remain to tell the story. Many walking tracks follow old tramway routes. The main timber dam in the upper reaches of Kaiarara Stream, one of the largest in New Zealand, is still in good condition. The New

View from Mt Hobson, with the Coromandel Peninsula in the distance. This area includes unique vegetation and petrel nesting areas.

Len Doel

Zealand Forest Service carried out major replanting of kauri and other native trees in the Great Barrier Forest Stewardship Area during the 1970s and early 1980s.

The extensive network of walking tracks and tramping routes throughout the forest caters for varying levels of fitness and experience, and there are camping sites and a hut for those who want an extended journey into the island's heartland. From Mt Hobson, it is possible to see as far as Auckland City and north to the Poor Knights Islands. The mountain can be climbed from the east via Windy Canyon, or the west alongside the Kaiarara Stream.

The Kaitoke Swamp is considered to be the highest-quality freshwater wetland in the Auckland region and one of the most significant in New Zealand. Nearly two-thirds is protected within the ecological area; the remainder is privately owned. Most of the swamp's catchment, including the slopes of Mt Hobson, is regenerating forest. Spotless crake, fernbird, banded rail and brown teal frequent the wetland areas. Underlying the layer of fresh water in the channels well away from the sea, tidal salt water supports a variety of marine fish, while freshwater fish occupy the upper level. Long-tailed bats have been observed around the fringes of the swamp.

The swamp is easily reached from either Whanga-parapara or the Whangaparapara Road, and thousands of visitors are attracted each year to the Peach Tree Hot Springs in the Kaitoke Stream. Raised boardwalks enable visitors to cross swampy areas with ease, and ensure vulnerable plants do not get trampled.

THE EAST COAST

Notable reserves along Great Barrier's eastern coast include the Whangapoua Stewardship Area, Rakitu Island Scenic Reserve, and the Okiwi, Awana and Harataonga Recreation Reserves.

The Whangapoua Stewardship Area was set aside as a reserve in the early 1990s and includes most of the estuary and associated wetlands, dunes and sandspit which back one of the island's finest ocean beaches. Brown teal forage and nest in the estuary and nearby. New Zealand dotterels breed on the sandspit, and at other sandy beaches along this coast. Visitors are asked to keep their distance from these shy, diminutive birds during their summer nesting season. Banded dotterel and the variable oystercatcher also breed here. The wrybill, South Island pied oystercatcher and eastern bar-tailed godwit are migrant visitors. Dogs and cats are a major threat to all these, and constant vigilance is needed to ensure people keep their dogs well away.

Offshore from Whangapoua Beach is Rakitu (Arid) Island, part pasture and part forest. Bought by the government in 1993, the Rakitu Recreation Reserve is Great Barrier's newest conservation land acquisition. The former farmer/owners have a lease to farm there until 2013. The 254-hectare island has eight threatened plant species, and its large areas of pasture make weed invasion of forest remnants a serious problem. In the future, the island's natural habitats may be restored and lost wildlife returned. Day visitors are welcome, but need to contact the farm manager on arrival, close gates and take care not to disturb stock. There are no tracks or other recreational facilities, and overnight stays are not permitted.

Arid Island, the most recently acquired conservation land in the Great Barrier area, has great promise as a future wildlife sanctuary.

Len Doel

South of Whangapoua, idyllic sandy coves and ocean surf beaches alternate with dramatic rocky headlands. Much of this spectacular landscape lies within the Harataonga Recreation Reserve, where a coastal walkway crosses the cliff tops. Four of the six campgrounds operated by DOC are located on this coast, near Whangapoua, Harataonga, Awana and Medlands Beaches. Dogs and other pets are not allowed.

Reserves like those at Okiwi and Awana (and Fitzroy Bay Landing and Bushs Beach on the west coast) are managed primarily for recreation.

VISITOR INFORMATION AND CODE OF CONDUCT

The DOC office near Port Fitzroy is the base for a handful of permanent staff and several temporary and seasonal workers. Staff are on 24-hour call for accidents and emergencies and to handle conservation offences. Information leaflets and maps can be obtained at DOC offices and various shops around the island. It is essential to book campground sites during the main summer holiday period.

Visitors are asked to observe the following code of conduct:

- Do not remove or disturb plants, animals, archaeological artifacts and historic features on conservation lands. They are protected by law.
- Do not disturb or harm native wildlife (including marine mammals) anywhere on and around the island.
- Do not light fires on conservation lands.
- Do not take dogs or other animals on to conservation lands or DOC campgrounds.
- Keep to the tracks and boardwalks.
- Do not disturb ground-nesting birds.
- Avoid bringing plants and pets to the island.
- Use boat flares only in emergencies.
- Camp only at permitted sites.
- Tell someone of your plans if walking one of the more rugged tracks.
- Always ask permission to go onto private land.

CHAPTER ELEVEN

INTO THE THIRD
MILLENNIUM

A thousand years from now, the odds are that Great Barrier will still be an island, with residents who will have their own ideas as to what happened or existed throughout the preceding millennium – perhaps expressed in a language we would only vaguely recognise today.

We are going through a period when great pressures are on our society to address and solve, as well and as quickly as we can, the general decline of our native and endemic species, and improve the health of the ecosystems in which they belong. Great Barrier stands apart from the mainland of New Zealand in having a much greater potential to meet that challenge: in fact, it is already well under way. Feral goats have been eliminated over the northern half of the island. The Auckland Regional Council and Department of Conservation are jointly carrying out a project to eradicate them from large areas in the south, while north of a line from Whangaparapara to Palmers Beach they are practically extinct.

Great Barrier and its associated smaller islands and islets ought to have an outstanding future. The forests are rapidly regenerating; some major predators and weeds found on the mainland are absent; the human population is low and a large part of the island is not available for future development. Furthermore, advances in technology (e.g. as a result of genome research) may allow quantum leaps forward in the management of pests and weeds. This may, for example, assist the present upward trend in the size of islands which can be kept free of rats.

While exotic animals kept by residents will always to some degree create problems, progress is being made. A recent very positive initiative has been bird-avoidance training for dogs to help reduce attacks, particularly on brown teal, black petrel and blue penguins. The technique has been increasingly used in other parts of New Zealand. Already most of the Great Barrier Island Hunting Club dogs have been through the programme. The first trial on the island in 2000 was initiated by the club with the full support of DOC, and run by Adele Smaill, of the Kiwi Recovery Programme on Coromandel Peninsula.

While dogs may be subject to retraining and testing, this promising programme itself is under trial to improve and refine its methodology.

By-laws and firm, fair and consistent animal-control measures appropriate for the island still remain of prime importance. It is vital that by-laws reflect the special environmental character of the island as well as promoting social harmony. Neutering of cats, as it becomes more widespread, will enable the feral population to be reduced or eliminated, while it is always good practice to keep domestic cats indoors by night and consider where they may go by day, because endangered species often are found close to human habitation and cats may travel long distances to hunt.

A major survey of island residents' attitudes to domestic, stray and feral cats and domestic dogs was being carried out as this book went to print. Under the auspices of the School of Environmental and Marine Sciences of the University of Auckland, the research project, a first for New Zealand, helps empower residents in deciding the future of their unique environment.

No country has a greater proportion of endangered species than New Zealand, which is probably why conservation techniques here are more advanced than perhaps anywhere else in the world. In the last decades of the Twentieth century, three distinct strategies were developed which gave New Zealand the potential to halt and roll back the tide of extinction.

First was the restoration of offshore islands by removing animal pests, and where necessary re-establishing natural forest cover along with native species which previously had declined or vanished, to re-establish ecological processes. Island wildlife sanctuaries started in 1894 when Little Barrier Island (Hauturu) came under protection by an act of Parliament. It was followed by other islands such as Maud, Mana, Codfish, Kapiti and Cuvier and, within the Hauraki

Task Force Green worker Ramon Richardson putting up bird count station indicators.

Little Windy Hill Company

Okiwi School children planting natives on a reserve adjacent to their school. Plants are grown from locally sourced seed.

Gulf, Tiritiri Matangi Island. There are many others.

Second, these techniques have been adapted on the mainland to create 'mainland islands'. These are of several kinds. Some are areas which have been totally freed of pests and surrounded by predator-proof fences (e.g. Karori Sanctuary in Wellington). A mainland island can also be created by intensively trapping an area for a time, then continuing to keep up the trapping pressure around its perimeter so in effect the traps function as a 'fence'. On Great Barrier this is being done to keep down rats and feral cats by the Little Windy Hill Company between Medlands Beach and Rosalie Bay, the Glenfern Sanctuary at Fitzroy, the Awana Catchment Trust, and the Benthorn Farm Sanctuary in Rosalie Bay. Many other projects are carried out by the island's schools and on many other private properties and particular areas of the DOC estates.

The third strategy has been the creation of marine reserves as breeding refuges and as representative examples of pristine, unexploited habitat. (The most famous is the highly successful marine reserve at Goat Island Bay, near Leigh, which attracts 250,000 visitors a year.) Planning for the Rakitu Marine Reserve on Great Barrier Island is under way, and other sites are being suggested as well. Marine reserves increase both the average size and density of fish species, while enhancing fish stocks for the recreational and commercial sector.

Another reason why Great Barrier needs to be protected is its size. Almost twice as large as the Auckland isthmus, it has a very wide range of ecosystems such as inland harbours, wetlands, dune systems and the mountainous interior. Other land islands in New Zealand are often comprised of single ecosystems such as Pureora Forest Sanctuary, while Great Barrier, surrounded by the sea, encompasses many — a valuable difference.

Weeds are another environmental issue, and on Great Barrier there are two strategies by which weed species are controlled or eliminated — either 'site-led' or 'weed-led'. A typical example of 'site-led' weed control is at Whangapoua estuary, where the South American pampas grass, among other species, is being eliminated to prevent it replacing native rush plants. 'Weed-led' programmes, on the other hand, aim to eradicate or contain particularly invasive weeds from the whole island before they become a bigger problem.

Then there are issues of inland waterways management. Appropriate culvert placement and design offers a better environment for waterfowl like brown teal, as well as providing fish-passes for freshwater species. The design of any structure across a waterway requires consideration of issues like these which can so easily be overlooked yet are not expensive to address.

There is potential to expand the extent and types of reserve. Rakitu (Arid) Island is now owned by DOC but leased out until 2013 under a 'sunset clause' which reaches a practical compromise with the island's previous owners. In the medium to long term this offers exciting possibilities for environmental restoration. In 1995 an unsuccessful attempt was made to purchase Kaikoura Island into public ownership, but this proposal may yet bear fruit in the longer term. Kaikoura would be a splendid prospect as a brown kiwi refuge against the bird's looming extinction on the mainland. Removing cats from this island should be relatively straightforward and inexpensive, and the birdlife there would subsequently flourish as it has done on other islands freed of cats.

In addition, beach and landcare groups are flourishing,

with both funding and other forms of assistance from Auckland City and the Auckland Regional Council. The Medlands and Awana Beach Care Groups are intensively involved in their areas. The three local schools each run a variety of projects including native tree propagation and planting-out, beach cleanups and monitoring projects, instilling a keen awareness of environmental issues in the upcoming generation and providing real hands-on experience of conservation, the benefits of which the children will see growing up with them.

New Zealand's Biodiversity Strategy outlines the loss of biological diversity and many of its causes, and suggests solutions. The strategy recognises the absolute importance of ensuring local communities become more familiar with their own environment. All would agree it is critical that government (DOC), regional (ARC) and local bodies (ACC) work with each other and together with the local community in addressing what the landmark 1997 State of the Environment Report warns us is 'our most pervasive environmental issue'.

The island has a constant uphill battle in the corridors of local-body power, for while there are 19 councillors in

Extraction of manuka oil for medicinal purposes offers potential for sustainable economic development.

Auckland, Great Barrier has only one representative and shares this with the more populous, almost suburban Waiheke Island, which for practical purposes is a world away. The representative sits monthly with five locally elected persons on the Great Barrier Island Community Board, who have a disproportionate burden upon them by virtue of the island's geography and isolation. Auckland City administrators' decisions have major impacts on the island. Community Board recommendations are not arrived at lightly, and are based on clear local knowledge of the island and its residents.

Finding out what species we have, and understanding the often complex and dynamic relationships between species and their role in terrestrial and marine ecosystems is an important part of making best use of limited resources such as people and money. Discoveries of entirely new species and known species not before found on Great Barrier have been made even while this book was being produced. There is much more to discover yet and there is always a need for more surveys. For instance, the discovery of the rare parasitic woodrose, expected to exist on the island, would assist in the search for the short-tailed bat. No matter what native flora or fauna is discovered or rediscovered, it will come as somewhat of a pleasant and at times exciting surprise.

The establishment of the Hauraki Gulf Marine Park in 2000 was an historic event ratifying a general consensus on the unique value of the gulf and its islands. The economic potential of the park and its single largest area of land, Great Barrier Island, should not be overlooked.

As Great Barrier's natural values become more widely recognised and pest control and eradication becomes more intensive, more jobs in that area are becoming available, especially to the many local residents already familiar with the local environment.

It is clear that we are only just starting to explore the potential of the eco-tourism market. The implications for Great Barrier residents and visitors and the island's economy and environment will be significant.

FURTHER READING

Anderson, A. 1989. *Prodigious birds. Moas and moa hunting in prehistoric New Zealand.* Cambridge University Press, Cambridge.

Anon., 1983. *The story of Hauraki Gulf Maritime Park.* Hauraki Gulf Maritime Park Board, New Zealand Department of Lands and Survey, Auckland.

Atkinson, I.A.E. 1978. Evidence for effects of rodents on the vertebrate wildlife of New Zealand islands. *In* P.R. Dingwall; I.A.E. Atkinson; C. Hay (Eds.). The ecology and control of rodents in New Zealand Nature Reserves. *New Zealand Department of Lands and Survey Information Series* No. 4: 7-30. Department of Lands and Survey, Wellington.

Atkinson, I.A.E. 1986. Rodents on New Zealand's northern offshore islands: distribution, effects and precautions against further spread. *In* Wright, A.E.; Beever, R.E. (eds.). The offshore islands of northern New Zealand. *New Zealand Department of Lands and Survey Information Series* No. 16: 13-40. Department of Lands and Survey, Wellington.

Atkinson, I.A.E. 1990. Ecological restoration on islands: Prerequisites for success. *In* D.R. Towns; C.H. Daugherty; I.A.E. Atkinson (Eds.). Ecological restoration of New Zealand islands. Conservation Sciences Publication No. 2: 73-90. New Zealand Department of Conservation, Wellington.

Atkinson, I.A.E.; Bell, B.D. 1973. Offshore and outlying islands. *In* G.R. Williams (Ed.). The natural history of New Zealand. An ecological survey, pp. 372-392. A.H. & A.W. Reed, Wellington.

Atkinson, I.A.E.; Millener, P.R. 1991. An ornithological glimpse into New Zealand's pre-human past. *Acta XX Congressus Internationalis Ornithologici*: 129-192.

Barrington, J. 1994. Aotea. The Barrier comes of age. *Forest & Bird* 273: 26-33.

Bartle, J.A. 1967. Records of Cook's petrels and black petrels from Great Barrier Island. *Notornis* 14: 26-27.

Bartlett, J.K. & Gardner, R.O. 1983. Flora of Great Barrier Island. *Auckland Botanical Society Bulletin* 14.

Beauchamp, A.J.; Chambers, R.; Kendrick, J.L. 1993. North Island weka on Rakitu Island. *Notornis* 40: 309-312.

Bell, B.D. 1976. Status of Great Barrier Island birds. *Notornis* 23: 310-319.

Bell, B.D.; Brathwaite, D.H. 1964. The birds of Great Barrier and Arid Islands. *Notornis* 10: 363-383.

Bellingham, P.J.; Hay, J.R.; Hitchmough, R.A.; McCallum, J. 1982. Birds of Rakitu (Arid) Island. *Tane* 28: 141-147.

Cameron, E.; Hayward, B.; Murdoch, G. 1997. *A field guide to Auckland. Exploring the Region's Natural and Historic Heritage.* Godwit, Auckland.

Cameron, E.K. & Wright, A.E. 1982. The vegetation and flora of Rakitu (Arid) Island, northern New Zealand. Tane 28: 85-124.

Child, J. 1974. *New Zealand Insects.* Fontana Periwinkle, Auckland.

Davidson, J. 1979. Archaic middens of the Coromandel Region: A review. *In* Anderson, A. (Ed.). Birds of a Feather: Osteological and archaeological papers from the South Pacific in honour of R.J. Scarlett. Pp. 183-202. *New Zealand Archaeological Association Monograph* 11. BAR International Series 62, Oxford.

Department of Conservation, 1996. Holidaymaker Map, 'Great Barrier Island', 336-02, Edition 1.

Gibbs, G. 1980. *New Zealand Butterflies.* Collins, Auckland.

Gibbs, G. 1998. *New Zealand Weta.* Reed, Auckland.

Gill, B. J. 1998. *Powell's Native Animals of New Zealand.* David Bateman, Auckland.

Gill, B. J., Whitaker, A.H. 1996. *New Zealand Frogs and Reptiles.* David Bateman, Auckland.

Gill, B.J. 1986. *Collins handguide to the frogs and reptiles of New Zealand.* Collins, Auckland

Great Barrier Island Committee of Inquiry. 1975. Report of the Great Barrier Island Committee of Inquiry (J. Granville, Chairman) July 1975. Report to the Minister of Works on the island's affairs and future. Town and Country Planning Branch, Ministry of Works and Development, Wellington.

Hamilton, W.M. (Ed.). 1961. Little Barrier Island (Hauturu). *New Zealand Department of Scientific and Industrial Research Bulletin 137.* Government Printer, Wellington.

Hay, J.R.; Douglas, M.E.; Bellingham, P. 1985. The North Island kokako *(Callaeas cinerea wilsoni)* on northern Great Barrier Island. *Journal of the Royal Society of New Zealand* 15: 291-293.

Hay, J.R.; Douglas, M.E.; Bellingham, P. 1985. The North Island kokako *(Callaeas cinerea wilsoni)* on northern Great Barrier Island. *Journal of the Royal Society of New Zealand* 15: 291-293.

Hayward, B.W. 1982. Offshore Islands Research Group trip to Rakitu (Arid) Island, northeast New Zealand, New Year 1980-1981. Introduction. *Tane* 28: 79-84.

Hayward, B.W. 1986. Prehistoric man on the offshore islands of northern New Zealand and his impact on the biota. *In* Wright, A.E.; Beever, R.E. (Eds.). The offshore islands of northern New Zealand. *New Zealand Department of Lands and Survey Information Series* No. 16: 139-152. Department of Lands and Survey, Wellington.

Heather, B.D.; Robertson, H.R. 1996. *The field guide to the birds of New Zealand.* Viking, Auckland.

Hitchmough, R.A. *Rattus rattus* from Rakitu (Arid) Island. *Tane* 33: 143-146.

Hutton, F.W. 1868. Notes on birds of Great Barrier Island. *Transactions and Proceedings of the New Zealand Institute* 1: 104-106.

Jordan, Helen. 1996. Great Barrier Island between the two World Wars: an outline of the history of the island with particular reference to the period 1918-1939. Unpublished research essay, University of Auckland.

Kauri Management Unit, Auckland Conservancy. 1979. *Great Barrier Island State Forest 1955. An Historical Account.* New Zealand Forest Service, Wellington.

Kirk, T. 1869. On the botany of Great Barrier Island. *Transactions New Zealand Institute* 1: 144-154.

de Lange, P.J., Heenan, P.B., Given, D.R., Norton, D.A., Ogle, C.C., Johnson, P.N. & Cameron, E.K. 1999. Threatened and uncommon plants of New Zealand. *New Zealand Journal of Botany* 37: 603-628.

Law, R.G. 1972. Archaeology at Harataonga Bay, Great Barrier Island. *Records of the Auckland Institute and Museum* 9: 81-123.

McCallum, J. 1983. A review of field club research on the northern offshore islands. *Tane* 29: 223-245.

McCallum, J. 1985. Unpublished report to the Secretary for Internal Affairs on the staus of seabirds and lizards of the islands lying off the south-western coast of Great Barrier Island. Department of Conservation file report.

McDowall, R.M. 2000. *The Reed field guide to New Zealand freshwater fishes.* Reed, Auckland.

Maddock, S; Whyte, D. 1966. *Islands of the Gulf.* Collins, Auckland.

Miller, D. 1984. *Common Insects in New Zealand.* Reed, Auckland.

Moore, L.B. 1973. Botanical notes on three high peaks overlooking the Hauraki Gulf. *Tane* 19: 213-220.

Morton, J.E. (Ed.). *A Natural History of Auckland.* Bateman, Auckland.

Ogle, C.C. 1980. Wildlife and wildlife habitat of Great Barrier Island, June 1980. *Fauna Survey Unit Report No. 24.* New Zealand Wildlife Service, Department of Internal Affairs, Wellington.

Ogle, C.C. 1981. Great Barrier Island wildlife survey. *Tane* 27: 177-200.

Orange, Claudia, 1990. The Maori People and the British Crown. *In* Keith Sinclair ed., *The Oxford Illustrated History of New Zealand,* Oxford University Press, Auckland.

Parkinson, B. 2000. *Field guide to New Zealand seabirds.* New Holland, Auckland.

Pickard C.R. & Towns, D.R. 1988. *Atlas of the amphibians and reptiles of New Zealand.* Department of Conservation, Wellington. publication No. 7, Wellington.

Reed, S.M. 1972. Report on Great Barrier Island, January 1972. *Notornis* 19: 274-276.

Spring-Rice, W. 1963. Harataonga – Great Barrier Island. *New Zealand Archaeological Association Newsletter* 6 (1): 24-27.

Tatton, Kim, 1994. The Settlement Archaeology of Aotea, Unpublished thesis, Department of Anthropology, University of Auckland.

Taylor, G.A.S. 1989. A register of northern offshore islands and a management strategy for island resources. *Department of Conservation Northern Region Technical Report Series No. 13,* May 1989. Department of Conservation, Northern Region, Auckland.

Towns D. R. 1985. A field guide to the lizards of New Zealand. New Zealand Wildlife Service, Department of Internal Affairs, Wellington.

Towns D.R. and McFadden I. 1993. Chevron skink recovery plan (*Leiolopisma homalonotum*). Threatened species recovery plan series no. 5. Department of Conservation, Wellington.

Towns, D.R. (Ed.). 1988. The natural history of Great Barrier Island. Collected papers from the Journal of the Royal Society of New Zealand. *Journal of the Royal Society of New Zealand* 3, May 1988.

Towns, D.R. 1988. Expedition to the northern block, Great Barrier Island, New Zealand. Introduction. Collected papers from the Journal of the Royal Society of New Zealand. *Journal of the Royal Society of New Zealand* 3, May 1988, pp. i-iii.

Turbott, E.G. 1990. Frederick Woolaston Hutton 1836-1905. *In* B.J. Gill & B.D. Heather (eds.). *A Flying Start. Commemorating fifty years of the Ornithological Society of New Zealand 1940-1990.* Random Century in association with the Ornithological Society of New Zealand, Auckland.

Veitch, C.R.; Bell, B.D. 1990. Eradication of introduced animals from the islands of New Zealand. *In* D.R. Towns; C.H. Daugherty; I.A.E. Atkinson (Eds.). *Ecological restoration of New Zealand islands.* Conservation Sciences Publication No. 2: 137-146. New Zealand Department of Conservation, Wellington.

Weetman, S. 1886. Notes on some moa remains found at the Great Barrier Island during February 1886. *Transactions of the New Zealand Institute* 19: 193-194.

Whitaker A. H. 1999. Lizards in the garden. *Forest and Bird,* November 1990, pages 14-17

Wright, A.E. & Cameron, E.K. 1985. Botanical features of northeastern Great Barrier Island, Hauraki Gulf, New Zealand. *Journal of the Royal Society 15*: 251-278.

Web Sites

Great Barrier Island visitor website: greatbarrier.co.nz

John Harrison's Aotea Great Barrier Island website: gbi.aotea.org

Judy Voullaire's Hauraki Gulf island website: haurakigulf.net/Islands.html

Auckland Regional Council website: arc.govt.nz

Auckland City Council website: akcity.govt.nz

Department of Conservation website: doc.govt.nz

In October 2001, students in schools around New Zealand can 'participate' in conservation research on Great Barrier Island during a LEARNZ virtual field trip: see learnz.org.nz/2001

CONTRIBUTORS

Don Armitage (general editor & Chapter 11)
Don Armitage is a Great Barrier Island resident, conservationist and former commercial fisherman. Among his eclectic interests he has sailed twice around the Pacific, scuba dived around much of New Zealand, dived commercially for paua at the Chatham Islands and held a pilot's licence. He is currently searching for new species on the island, in particular long-tailed bats.

Rod Clough (Chapter 1)
Director of Clough & Associates Ltd, a heritage consultancy set up in 1995 to offer a range of services relating to cultural resource management. These include resource consent assessments, archaeological survey and mitigation investigations, and conservation/management plans. Previously an archaeologist at the University of Auckland.

Brenda Sewell (Chapter 2)
Archaeologist since the 1980s with the Historic Places Trust, Department of Conservation, and now a consultant. Author of many reports on Maori sites in Auckland province. Has carried carrying out historic research for DOC on the copper industry, gum digging and timber extraction on Great Barrier Island.

Phil Moore (Chapter 3)
Studied geology at the University of Auckland and now a consultant/researcher and Principal of Peninsula Research. Has co-authored papers on the geology of Great Barrier and books on popular geology including *Vanishing Volcanoes. A guide to the landforms and rock formations of Coromandel Peninsula* and *Coromandel Gold. A guide to the historic goldfields of Coromandel Peninsula.*

John Ogden (Chapter 4)
Associate Professor (Forest Ecology), School of Biological Sciences, University of Auckland.

Research interests include ecosystem conservation and pest and weed impacts on native ecosystems. He has a house on Great Barrier.

Ewen Cameron (Chapter 5)
Curator of Botany at the Auckland Museum in charge of the Herbarium. With more than 20 years' experience working with the flora of northern New Zealand, he has published several papers on the flora and vegetation on Great Barrier Island.

Peter Maddison (Chapter 6)
Entomologist with Landcare Research, Auckland, and closely involved with Forest & Bird.

Alina Arkins (Information on bats in Chapter 6)
Recently completed her Master's degree at Auckland University, studying the diet and activity patterns of short-tailed bats on Little Barrier Island. Now self-employed as an ecological consultant, specialising in bat research projects.

Graham Ussher (Chapter 7)
Herpetologist at the School of Environmental and Marine Sciences, University of Auckland Auckland, lecturing in restoration ecology. Has extensively worked with New Zealand reptile fauna (including tuatara, skinks and geckos) as project co-ordinator, scientific advisor or field assistant.

Bob Creese (Chapter 8)
Formerly director of the Leigh Marine Laboratory (University of Auckland); now Principal Research Scientist with the Office of Conservation, NSW in Australia. His research interests include ecological processes on intertidal rocky shores and in estuaries; marine reserves, threats of introduced marine species, species enhancement and habitat restoration.

Bob McDowall (Information on freshwater fish in Chapter 8)
Recently retired from the National Institute of

Marine and Freshwater Research in Christchurch, Dr McDowall has for many years been the foremost authority on freshwater fishes of New Zealand. He is the author of numerous research papers and books and regularly contributes articles to magazines on issues related to freshwater fishing.

Tim Lovegrove (Chapter 9) Currently Natural Heritage Scientist at Auckland Regional Council. Previously employed with Department of Conservation on kakapo programme on Little Barrier Island, and with former Department of

Lands and Survey and Wildlife Service researching bird transfers on the Hauraki Gulf islands and Kapiti Island.

Annie Wheeler (Chapter 10) Has worked for 10 years with the Department of Conservation Auckland Conservancy in a variety of roles including media and community liaison, publications, Auckland Conservation Management Strategy (CMS), strategic planning. Involved with public consultation process and hearings on Great Barrier Island during preparation of CMS.

GENERAL INDEX

INDEX OF SCIENTIFIC NAMES